TOOLS FOR HEALTH AND HEALING GOD'S WAY

Truth & Knowledge

S:S *Barbara* Vol. 1

W.F. D.H.

Dr. James A. Dail, Sr.

Reformation Healing Ministries International
Monroe, NC 28112
www.jamesdailministries.org

"Our people are dying for lack of KNOWLEDGE."
Hosea 4:6a

"And ye shall know the TRUTH, and the TRUTH shall make you free."
St. John 8:32

Published by Reformation Healing Ministries International
Monroe, NC 28112

Published in the United States of America.
ISBN 978-0-9817461-0-4

TABLE OF CONTENTS

PREFACE

I am so excited that you have chosen the journey to optimal health and wellness. No matter what your condition may be, we are confident in God and the knowledge He has given us, that you can be completely well. God has equipped your body with everything needed to heal itself when guided in the right direction.

In this volume, you will learn about some of the harmful, disease-producing foods and chemicals that you digest on a daily basis. However, I ask that you do not focus on the things you will have to eliminate from your diet; instead, concentrate on all the incredible, life-changing health benefits you will gain.

It takes six times the nutrients to heal than to prevent. It took many years to get you where you are physically, spiritually, and emotionally. Be patient and diligent until you arrive at your new destination.

Allow this book to jump-start your new lifestyle. We pray that you keep the faith and believe God for the ultimate healing of your body, mind, and soul

Blessings Always,

Dr. James A. Dail, Sr.
Founder/Overseer
Reformation Healing Ministries International

THE HEALTHY PERSPECTIVE

"Our people are dying for lack of knowledge." **Hosea 4:6a**

It is critically important that we take responsibility for our bodies. We need to have knowledge, Godly wisdom, and counsel on honing this body (temple) by caring for it and creating a lifestyle that glorifies God. Psalm 139:14 says we were *"Fearfully and wonderfully made: marvelous are thy works."* As we learn and understand that the human body is the wonderful work of God's hand, formed in His image and likeness; we will then seek to bring it into subjection. The body is a wonderful structure given to us by God to take steward and charge over, and to keep in harmonious action.

In our Christian teachings, we are told that honoring and glorifying the body includes avoiding adultery, fornication, lusts of the flesh, and other sins. It is unfortunate that, all too often, the importance of nutrition and a healthy lifestyle such as proper eating, rest, and exercise are left out of the teachings. First Thessalonians 5:23 lets us know that God wants our whole spirit, soul, and body to be preserved blameless unto the coming of our Lord Jesus Christ.

First Corinthians 6:19 and 20 tells us that our bodies are not our own to treat as we please, to cripple by habits that lead to decay, making it impossible to render to God perfect service. We were bought with a price; and our lives and all our faculties belong to Him. He is caring for us every moment. He keeps the living machinery in action. If we were left to run it for one moment, we would die. It is through Him that we live, breathe, and have our being. We are absolutely dependent on God. Our soul, body, and spirit belong to Him. God gave His only begotten Son for the body as well as for the soul. Our entire life belongs to Him to for His service so that we may glorify Him through exercising every faculty He has given us.

The wonderful mechanism of the human body does not receive half of the care as is often given to personal possessions, such as our automobiles. We are willing to spend extra money to put high-test fuel in our automobiles; yet, we put large amounts of destructive trash in our bodies—items that we have the nerve to call food. These "things" that we ingest break down the body and mind and cause them to dysfunction, creating sickness, diseases, and premature death.

We have an obligation to God to present Him with clean, pure, and healthy bodies. When we choose the Will of God and are conformed to the character of Christ, the Spirit can act through our organs and faculties. The Spirit of Christ is to take possession of the organs of speech and our mental, physical, and moral powers.

Many times, we argue that we can do destructive things to our body because "we have to die from something." Therefore, we try to justify destructive eating habits and lifestyles such as, eating twinkies, swine, and all manners of pork, processed foods, sugars and other things of the world. First John 2:15 and 16 instructs us to *"Love not the world, neither the things that are in the world. If any man loves the world, the love of the Father is not in him. For all that is in the world, the lust of the flesh, and the lust of the eyes and the pride of life, is not of the Father, but of the world."* Genesis 1:29 says, *"And the Lord said, 'Behold, I have given you every herb bearing seed, which is upon the face of all the earth, and every tree, in the which is the fruit of a tree yielding seed; to you it shall be for meat.'"*

We must be diligent in our conviction to honor the body (temple) without excuse. It is not unlawful to go out and eat a hamburger. However, by eating it, you will suffer the consequences of the fat, salt, and blood it contains. First Corinthians 6:12 says, *"Everything is permissible for me; but not everything is beneficial. Everything is permissible for me, but I will not be mastered by anything."* Are you a slave to your appetite? One of the ploys of the devil is reflected in how deadly foods are manufactured to be pleasing to the eye through packaging, preservatives, flavor enhancers, and food colorings.

Wholeness and holy is a journey. First Thessalonians 5:23 reads, *"And the very God of peace sanctify you holy."* Paul was giving his final exaltation to the Church of Thessalonica when he told the brothers what they needed to do and how they needed to preserve their existence and their wholeness in their lives. And Paul said, "I pray God your whole spirit and soul and body be preserved blameless upon the coming of our Lord Jesus Christ."

You see folks, the word "blameless" means without defect. Paul knew if you had defects in your body because of neglect and the lack of knowledge. As it states in Hosea 4:6, your body would be unacceptable to God. Romans 12:1 reads, "*I beseech you, therefore, brothers by the mercies of God, that you present your bodies a living sacrifice, holy and acceptable to God as your reasonable service.*" Now, without what? Blemish! Paul knew that God would not accept anything sacrificed to him with blemishes. Everything that is a sacrifice to God has to be whole or without defect. The devil's job is to convince you to do things within your life so that your lifestyle or life will not exact wholeness. Therefore, if you do not have wholeness, then you are not seeking holiness. In Romans 12:2 , Paul said, "*And be not conformed to this world, but be ye transformed by the renewing of your mind, that ye may prove what is that good, and acceptable, and perfect, will of God.*"

Let us look at Romans 10:13, which is on what the Christian church is based upon. The Christian church is taught that whosoever shall call upon the name of the Lord shall be saved. Jesus died for our salvation. We all know that salvation means saved, right? Now, saved in Strong's number 4982 and Romans 10:13 means, "To save, to keep safe and sound; to rescue from danger or destruction, from injury or peril; to save a suffering from disease, to make well, to restore the health, to make whole, to heal the whole body." So now, are you completely saved? In Matthew, Jesus says, "*Heaven is at hand, heaven is within you.*" God knew that without having heaven in you on earth, there is no way that you could do His perfect will. Why? Because you need a healthy body to effectively do God's Will.

STATEMENT OF FAITH for
Reformation Healing Ministries International

Preamble

Reformation Healing Ministries International's (RHMI) goals and objectives are to promote good health and long life according to God's Word. RHMI introduces the Biblical, systematic, nutritional plan that God provided with specific teachings, guidelines, and directions on caring for the temple of God in order to live life based on God's promise. *"And the LORD said,* **'My Spirit shall not strive with man forever, for he is indeed flesh; yet his days shall be one hundred and twenty years'"** (Genesis 6:3).

The health of a Christian's physical body is as much a part of the Gospel—the Good News—as the health of the Spirit and the health of the Soul. God wants a healthy triune man: healthy *Body*, healthy *Spirit*, and healthy *Soul*. Knowing this truth, the writer of the Gospel of John declares to us in a letter: *"Beloved, I wish above all things that thou mayest prosper and be in health, even as thy soul prospereth"* (3 John 2).

The Strong's Exhaustive Concordance of the Bible (Strong) explains that the Greek word *hugiaino* translated into English is *health*. From hugiaino we derive the word hygiene. Hugiaino or hygiene means "to have sound health and to be well in body." Figuratively, Strong explains that health means "being uncorrupted or being true in doctrine, as well as being true in the Word of God."

Beloved, let the Word of God be your God. Do not let your belly be your God. If you eat what God tells you not to eat, it grieves God. Just as it grieved the Apostle Paul who wrote, *"For many walk, of whom I have told you often, and now tell you even weeping, that they are the enemies of the cross of Christ: whose end is*

destruction, whose god is their belly" (Philippians 3:18c-19b).
Therefore, beloved, we of RHMI pray to our Father who art in heaven, that above all things, you may prosper, be in health, uncorrupted, true to Biblical doctrine, even as your soul prospers.

We pray health to you in the Name of Jesus, The Christ. Amen.

The Body of Christ...

"Prayer is the utmost responsibility of the children of God. Communicating with God, the Father, through prayer is the foundation of life. RHMI and the members of the Body of Christ will uphold their responsibility to God through prayer."
—Dr. James A. Dail, Sr.

"And all things, whatsoever ye shall ask in prayer, believing, ye shall receive" (Matthew 21:22).

1. We believe (faith) in God the Father, the Creator, the Almighty, the Sustainer, and the Reformer of heaven and earth.

2. We believe (faith) in God the Father, the Creator, Jesus The Christ, our resurrected Savior and LORD, and the only begotten Son of God.

3. We believe (faith) in God, the Creator, and the Holy Spirit, the Comforter and Truth, who is sent to live beside our spirit.

4. We believe (faith) in the Father, The Son, and The Holy Spirit (the Triune God, The Holy Trinity)—and that these three are One. Jesus declares in John 10:30, "*I and My Father are one!*" Moreover, Jesus declares in John 4:24, "*God is Spirit, and those who worship Him must worship in spirit and in truth.*"

5. We believe (faith) in the redemption, forgiveness, and salvation provided by the sacrificial blood of Jesus of Nazareth at Calvary's Cross. This is our gospel, our good

news, *"For God so loved the world that He gave His only begotten Son, that whosoever believes in Him should not perish but have everlasting life"* (John 3:16).

6. We believe (faith) that the Holy Scriptures are God-breathed, inspired, infallible, and are most worthy for instruction, healing, and blessing. *"All Scripture is given by inspiration of God, and is profitable for doctrine, for reproof, for correction, for instruction in righteousness that the man of God may be complete, thoroughly equipped for every good work"* (2 Timothy 3:16-17). Being healthy based on the gospel is a good work. The Scriptures teach practices that promote, maintain, and restore health. These healthy scriptural practices include faith, diet, prayer, fasting, laying on of hands, exercise, tithing, giving, and more.

7. "Faith is action, based upon belief, is supported by confidence that God's Word is true. The ABC's of faith are Action, Belief, and Confidence" (The late Dr. Gene Scott). RHMI and the members of the Body of Christ believe and know that it takes more than just belief to please God. *"Even so faith, if it hath not works, is dead, being alone"* (James 2:17). RHMI takes Faith and Action, based upon Belief and supported by Confidence, that God's Word is true. Faith and Works that follow the Word of God lead to healing.

8. Tithing and Giving are ordained by God. The Bible says, ***"Bring all the tithes into the storehouse, that there may be food in My house, and try Me now in this, Says the Lord of hosts. If I will not open for you the windows of heaven and pour out for you such a blessing that there will not be room enough to receive it."*** We believe that 'Stewardship of our money' is the ability to manage our finances so that we do not hold back what God expects us to give for the building of His physical and spiritual Kingdom on earth. *"And Jesus went about all the cities and villages, teaching in their synagogues, preaching the gospel of the kingdom, and healing every sickness and every disease among the people"* (Matthew 9:35). RHMI

hope that you realize that God places less importance on the monetary value of the gift, and more importance on the sacrifice involved. (See Luke 21:1-4). By giving your tithes and offerings, you bless God. *"Bless the LORD, O my soul: and all that is within me, bless His holy name. Bless the LORD, O my soul, and forget not all His benefits: Who forgiveth all thine iniquities; who healeth all thy diseases"* (Psalm 103:1-3).

9.   We believe (faith) that we are beings created by God. *"So God created mankind in His own image; in the image of God He created him; male and female He created them"* (Genesis 1:27). Since God created mankind, God knows what is best for our health and well-being. God created our body, soul, and spirit. Each of our parts must be in harmony with God's principles for optimum health. To keep our health from failing, RHMI and the members of the Body of Christ regularly read and reread the instruction manual for mankind—the Holy Bible. Then we do what the Bible says to do from the beginning to the end.

10. We believe (faith) that we are called beings. We have a God-ordained employment—to obey God and to serve Him. Jesus said, ***"I have not come to call the righteous, but sinners, to repentance"*** (Luke 5:32). ***"No one can come to Me*** (Jesus) ***unless the Father who sent Me draws him"*** (John 6:44a). Mankind has a God-given purpose. *"... **You shall love the LORD your God with all your heart, with all your soul, and with all your mind"*** (Matthew 22:37). Jesus said, ***"If you love Me, keep My commandments"*** (John 14:15). *"... **He** (or she) **who is greatest among you shall be your servant"*** (Matthew 23:11).

11. We believe (faith) that we are responsible stewards. God has entrusted His earthly creation—including our bodies—into our care as His stewards and servants. *"Then God blessed them (the male and female Adam, mankind), and said to them, '**Be fruitful and multiply; fill the earth and subdue it: have dominion over the fish of the sea, over the birds of the***

air, and over every living thing that moves on the earth'" (Genesis 1:28).

"Stewardship of our body" is being able to manage our body well so that we are mentally and physically able to do what God expects for the building of His physical and spiritual Kingdom here on earth.

The members of the Body of Christ believe that responsible stewardship of our bodies will help us get much closer to living the 120 healthy years for which God gave us license. *"And the LORD said, 'My Spirit shall not strive with man forever, for he is indeed flesh; yet his days shall be one hundred and twenty years'"* (Genesis 6:3).

12. We believe (faith) that we are responsible for our own health. We believe physical health is primarily a reflection of God's universal law of cause and effect. *"Do not be deceived, God is not mocked; for whatever a man sows, that he will also reap"* (Galatians 6:7). How we feed and care for ourselves does indeed impact our health and the health of our offspring.

13. We believe (faith) that God has, does, and will directly intervene in order to heal, according to His sovereign purpose. God said, *"...If you diligently heed the voice of the Lord your God and do what is right in His sight, give ear to His commandments and keep all His statutes, I will put none of the diseases on you which I have brought on the Egyptians. For, I am the LORD who heals you"* (Exodus 15:26).

14. We believe (faith) that Satan, our adversary, seeks to destroy us. We believe in the existence of Satan, his demons, and evil spirits who can be witches. We believe that given the opportunity, satanic forces will use every means possible, especially undermining our health to disrupt and destroy the lives of us who seek to love and obey God. *"Be self-controlled, be watchful; because your adversary the devil walks about like a roaring lion, seeking whom he may devour"* (1 Peter 5:8).

"God resists the proud, but gives grace to the humble. Therefore, submit to God. Resist the devil, and he will flee from you" (James 4:6b-7).

15. We believe (faith) that physical health is an important factor towards effective service. A body in ill-repair or diseased has a diminished capacity for effective service. Research from Duke University Medical Center confirms that Faith can speed up recovery, and a lack of Faith can cause slow recovery from diseases.

16. We believe (faith) that optimum health is built upon seven essentials. In order to maintain optimal physical health, one must have pure air, pure water, health-promoting food, adequate exercise, sufficient rest (6.50 to 7.00 hours daily), and be obedient to God's Word by tithing and giving. In addition, one must learn how to effectively handle stress. *"Cease from anger, and forsake wrath; do not fret (stress out), it only causes harm"* (Psalm 37:8).

17. We believe (faith) that health-promoting foods come primarily from the garden. A healthy diet centers on fruits, vegetables, and grains consumed in forms closest to their original state and free of chemical additives. *"And God said,* ***See, I have given you every herb that yields seed which is on the face of all the earth, and every tree whose fruits yields seed; to you it shall be for meat"*** (Genesis 1:29).

18. We believe (faith) that invasive health care measures such as surgery and other medical procedures are sometimes necessary. We believe (faith) that invasive measures do not heal. Healing comes from the body's own God-given healing mechanisms.

19. We believe (faith) that spiritual health is of ultimate importance. Physical health is very important, but it is a means to an end, not an end in itself. Man was created to love, obey, and serve God. *"If you love Me (Jesus), **keep my commandments"*** (John 14:15).

20. We believe (faith) that Love of God and Love for others is of ultimate importance for spiritual, mental, and physical healing. Love is the single most important commandment in the scriptures. Jesus taught that the single greatest commandment in the Bible is to love God with all your heart, mind, soul, and strength. He followed up by saying that the second greatest commandment draws from the first—*"**Love your neighbor as yourself.**"*

"For God so loved the world that He gave His only begotten Son, that whosoever believeth in Him should not perish, but have everlasting life" (John 3:16).

"Let love be without dissimulation. Abhor that which is evil; cleave to that which is good. Be kindly affectioned one to another with brotherly love; in honor preferring one another; not slothful in business; fervent in spirit; serving the Lord; rejoicing in hope; patient in tribulation; continuing instant in prayer; distributing to the necessity of saints; given to hospitality. Bless them which persecute you: bless, and curse not. Rejoice with them that do rejoice, and weep with them that weep" (Roman 12:9-15).

Of what profit is it if an individual gets well physically and yet has neither peace with God, nor a sense of purpose for his life? We believe that the church should teach the people of God how to remove physical and spiritual roadblocks to fulfill the will of God.

*"And He (Jesus) said to them, '**Go into all the world and preach the gospel to every creature. He who believes and is baptized will be saved; but he who is not-believing will be condemned**'"* (Mark 16:15-16).

*The Biblical references, quotes, and translations in this document are taken from the King James and the New King James Versions of the Holy Bible. *

OUR VISION...

of Reformation Healing Ministries is to minister to those from all walks of life who are suffering in their bodies.

OUR MISSION...

of Reformation Healing Ministries is to be a multifaceted resource to train, educate, and disseminate information locally and nationally on how and why proper diet, food preparation and lifestyle changes will greatly reduce the chance of sickness and diseases and enormously increase health, wellness, learning, fitness and proper behavior. All forms of communication, including the Internet, television, radio, seminars, workshops, and educational materials will be utilized to facilitate this objective.

We will not discriminate against anyone.

OUR GOAL...

at Reformation Healing Ministries is to be living epistles and creditable witnesses to those who have sicknesses and diseases in their bodies. Since we believe that our body is the temple of God and His Spirit dwells in us, we feel that it is our purpose to educate the Body of Christ about various diseases, illnesses, bad diets, and improper eating habits. *"We have an adversary called the devil, and his job is to destroy our temple"* (John 10:10).

It is our goal to inform God's people and equip them to have good health.

JESUS' GUIDELINES FOR EATING

The following information was extracted from the *Dead Sea Scrolls*, by Mr. Edmond Bordeaux Szekely and quoted from *The Essene Gospel of Peace*. *The Essene Gospel of Peace* is a book that was put together by the Essene—ministers of peace who spent a great deal of time studying the writings of the ancients—here in this country. Bible history said that Jesus was part of the Essene's Sect.

The *Dead Sea Scrolls* is more than 2,000 years old and is currently under lock and key in the Vatican. There was a tour of the *Dead Sea Scrolls* exhibition held in the United States (US)that was safely protected and guarded with tight security. The following is what Jesus said according to the *Dead Sea Scrolls*:

> *Eat only when called by the angel of appetite. Cook not, neither mix all things with one another, lest your bowels become as steaming bogs.*

> *Be content with two or three sorts of foods, which you will always find around you. Never eat unto fullness. Satan and his power tempt you to eat more and more. But live by the spirit and resist the desires of the body.*

> *Your fasting is always pleasing in the eyes of the angels of God. So give heed to how much you have eaten when you are sated (satisfied), and eat less always by a third. Let the weight of your daily food be not less than a mina (a Hebrew weight approximately 99/100ths of a pound), but mark that it not go beyond two (i.e., between one and two pounds of food a day).*

> *Trouble not the work of the angels in your body by eating often. For I tell you truly, he who eats more than twice in the day does in him the work of Satan.*

Eat only when the sun is highest in the heavens, and once again when it is set. And if you will that Satan shuns you afar, then sit but once in the day at the table of God.

Eat not unclean foods brought from afar, but eat what your trees bear, for your God knows what is needful of you, and where, and when.

Eat not as the heathen do, who stuff themselves in haste, defiling their bodies with all manner of abomination.

Eat always from the table of God: the fruit of the trees, the grasses and the grains of the field, the milk of beasts (goat milk), and the honey of bees. For everything beyond these is of Satan, and leads by the way of sins and diseases unto death.

Breathe long and deeply with all your meals, and chew well your food with your teeth, that it becomes water, and that the angel of water turns it to blood in your body. And eat slowly, as it were a prayer you make to the Lord. For I tell you truly, the power of God enters into you, if you eat after this manner but Satan turns into a steaming bog the body of him upon whom the angels of air (breathing long and deeply at meals) and water (chewing food into a liquid) do not descend at his repasts.

Put naught upon the alter of the Lord when your spirit is vexed, neither think upon anyone with anger in the temple of God. And enter only unto the Lord's sanctuary when you feel in yourselves the call of his angels, for all that you eat in sorrow, or in anger, or without desire, becomes a poison in your body.
Place with joy your offerings upon the alter of your body. Remember every seventh day is holy and consecrated to God. On six days feed your body with the gifts of the earthly Mother, but on the seventh day sanctify your body for your

heavenly Father. On the seventh day, eat not any earthly food,
but live only upon the words of God.

The scientists of today had no clue that Jesus was teaching this. Based on research, today's scientists came up with the same program and process of these guidelines including, not eating under stress, chewing your food, eating the right food, and not eating when angry. These guidelines are the same as what Jesus taught over 2,000 years ago.

HEALING IS GOD'S DESIRE FOR HIS CHILDREN

In Psalms 103:3, the Word of God says, "*Who forgiveth all thine iniquities; who healeth all thy diseases.*" If the Word of God is true, that means that God will heal all of your diseases. We have taken that verse and put all the healing of disease in the hands of God. However, God has put some of that responsibility in our hands by creating an environment within the body that will allow it to heal itself if we remove the impurities.

For example, if you put a gun to your head with a bullet in it and pull the trigger, God is not going to stop the bullet because that is your choice. If you take a fork with poison on it that you call it "food," and enter it into your mouth, God is not going to knock that so-called "food" out of your hands to stop the disease.

Although God has created a healing environment within the body, He has also given us choices. We have a choice to live or die. If God said that He would heal all our diseases, why do people in the world (doctors) say that certain diseases are incurable? Many people believe the world and not God. Not believing in the Word of God is causing disease in our body. We are the ones who put the things in our body which manifest themselves as disease.

Several individuals are influenced by the world system and believe that some diseases cannot be healed or prevented. We need to teach the cause of disease. In this book, you will learn that dairy, meat, sugar, food additives, etc., are some of the weapons the devil uses to harm the human body. In order for us to heal those diseases, we first have to remove them from our bodies. Anything that we do to cause diseases in our body is a sin.

Every time Jesus healed, He advised the person that "he is healed, to go and sin no more." If the choices that you make with your spirit, mind, and body are the opposite of righteousness, then they are sin. James 4:17 reads, "*Therefore to him that knoweth to do good, and doeth it not, to him it is sin.*" Most churches know that sweet foods, canned sodas, fast foods, and fried foods are not good for us. What is the difference between fast food and the foods in your kitchen? It is the same thing, but you just get the food faster from the restaurants.

In order to create an environment in your body so it can actually heal; you have to eliminate all those impurities. One reason pastors are not successful in healing is because they do not have faith. God heals divinely; and the person whom He uses to deliver the healing has to have faith in His healing process.

Matthew 17:15-20 talks about a father who took his son to the Disciples of Christ to get him healed. He was a lunatic that suffered from either schizophrenia or bipolar disorder. The demon was in his mind. The disciples could not heal him. However, after they took him to Jesus, he was healed. The disciples asked Jesus why they could not heal him; and Jesus said, "*Lack of faith*." They did not believe that the young man could be healed because he had a severe case of the disease.

If a person does not believe that healing can take effect, then it will not happen no matter how much lying of the hands or sprinkling of oil on the body has taken place. God heals in the state of wholeness. Ninety percent of what Jesus did on earth was to heal and show the church that God is in the "healing business."

In John 9, Jesus instructed a young, blind man on what he needed to do to regain his sight. God wants us to know that we have some responsibility in the whole healing process. The church has to regain faith. It is hard for a pastor to have faith that a church member can be healed of arthritis, diabetes, high blood pressure, cancer, and other diseases if he/she also has those diseases. In the pastor's heart and soul, he/she will not believe the church member can be healed if the pastor has been trying for years to heal him/herself. If the pastor is sick, how can God work through him/her to touch you, yet leave the pastor in the state of disease? We have the healing power, but cannot exercise it if we do not believe (Faith). The world has already told us that high blood pressure, diabetes, cancer, arthritis, and lupus cannot be healed; therefore, we immediately believe that. God never said that diseases are incurable.

We have to regain our faith and trust in God and not rely on the world. God has put every disease in front of me as I visit churches all over the world; and every disease has been reversed. I have total faith that healing will take effect. After I inform my patients on what caused the disease in the first place, I give them directions on the path to reversing the disease. I encourage them to make changes in their lifestyle to prevent diseases that are destroying the sanctuary of God. The church needs to accept God's healing principles.

Hindrance to Healing

There are some hindrances that block our path to healing, including:

1) ***Unconfessed sins*** (James 5:6)—It is important to confess our sins and move forward. If you do something against the body that is not righteousness, then it is sin. If you are consuming food that is causing harm to the body, then it is sin. You need to confess and repent.

2) ***Demonic oppression or bondage*** (Luke 13:11-13)—For example, we are in bondage when we believe that the devil is going to heal us. The devil inspired the health care system, as John states in Revelation 18:23, "*The great merchants of the world will deceive all nations with their sorcery.*" The terms "sorcery," "pharmacy," and "witchcraft" all mean the same in the Word of God. We are locked into a health care system that we think we need because it is, for the most part, readily-accessible and free (Medicare and Medicaid). Many doctors drug the body with medications filled with harmful side effects. Health means "void of disease." Having side effects from something is like using the witch's potion.

3) ***Fear or acute anxiety*** (Proverbs 3:5-8 & Phil 4:6-7)—Fear stops the immune system and is the foundation of stress. When the immune system shuts down, then anything can be absorbed in the body to cause disease. The immune system is our prevention mechanism to fight off the wiles of the devil. The devil tries to breach the immune system so that disease can penetrate God's sanctuary.

4) ***Past disappointments*** (Mark 5:26 & John 5:5-7)—Many people give up after seeking treatment for a disease from medical doctors. Past disappointments will shut us down from

recognizing new things that God put into our lives to generate healing in our bodies.

5) **People** will block your healing (Mark 10:48)—People can discourage you from trying natural healing. Even though I have been recognized all over the world, several individuals who come to my clinic have told me that others have tried to convince them otherwise. God had to tell his people (in Jeremiah 46:11) that all the medicine in the world is not going to heal their bodies; rather, they would have to go to the balm of Gilead (a sap from the tree). Why should we try to dissuade people from going through the natural way of healing?

6) **Carnal Behavior** (I Corinthians 11: 29-30)—For example, when we get a headache we take aspirin, or women with PMS take Motrin. Many individuals turn to medication to solve all their health problems. Aspirin causes several side effects and diseases in the body. Changing your lifestyle and using natural remedies are the safest options. It is unfortunate that we do things based on the world system and not God's.

7) **Lack of Faith (Unbelief)** is a hindrance to healing (Mark 6:3-6; 9:19, 23-24)—As mentioned earlier, if the healer does not believe that you can be healed, then you will not be healed (Matthew 17:15-20). Even though many people have witnessed God's healing power through His vessels, many Pastors and Elders of the church still do not believe.

PRAYER IS THE FOUNDATION OF HEALTH AND HEALING

Prayer is the foundation of everything that we do. Communicating with God is something special that we need to purpose in our hearts to do several times a day. One of the problems we face in dealing with disease is that we do not put enough emphasis on prayer.

Prayer is, and will continue to be, a major source of our healing. Universities throughout the country who have conducted research on prayer and healing have found that prayer is the basis of everything in our lives, especially concerning healing. At Reformation Healing Ministries International, we promote and teach the importance of health through of the Word of God, and the science of the way a person's body physically, emotionally, and spiritually responds to prayer. Research proves that prayer works 100 percent of the time in our lives.

It is important to understand what the Word of God states about prayer. Psalms 66:18 tells us, "*If I regard iniquity in my heart, the Lord will not hear me.*" For example, those who take pleasure in unrighteousness have no hope of answered prayer when they call on God. He wants us to separate from sins, and only then will He respond to us as a Father to his Son (See 2 Corinthians 6:14-18, James 4:3, and I John 3:2).

Many people who pray for others have not separated themselves from sin. When we are sick, we have a tendency to revert to prayer, which we should; but we have not turned around our sinful ways and accepted righteousness. God cannot hear us until we separate from sins.

James 5:16 informs us that, "*The effectual fervent prayer of a righteous man availeth much.*" Prayer is the foundation. Our healing process does not start until we communicate with our Father. We are fortunate to be able to communicate with God in prayer. He has so much love for us that He gave us His "only begotten Son." It is a special privilege to have a Father like God in our hearts.

Matthew 21:22 lets us know that, "*And all things, whatsoever ye shall ask in prayer, believe and you will receive.*" Mark 9: 24-26 reads, "*When Jesus saw that the people came running together, he rebuked the unclean spirit, saying unto him, Thou dumb and deaf spirit, I charge thee, come out of him, and enter him no more. And the spirit cried out, convulsed him greatly, and came out of him. And when He had come out and entered into the house, the disciples asked Him privately, why could we not cast him out. He said to them that this kind can come out by nothing but prayer.*"

Disease is something of the earth. It is something the devil has placed in our lives, which means we have made bad choices and decisions, for the most part, based on lack of knowledge or understanding. The ignorance of life is that we have placed ourselves in the position to be diseased. When you pray, go into your room and pray to the Father who is in that secret place. He will reward you openly.

As I minister and talk to individuals who come to me with an illness or disease, I never let them leave without a word of prayer. That is the way it should be every time you go to someone who is professing to be a vessel of healing through Christ Jesus. If they are treating your body and will not pray for you, then you should find another health care practitioner. Prayer is paramount. It is the foundation of everything represented in that visit. Prayer works in a divine way. It is the first thing a holistic practitioner needs to introduce to you.

A study done by the University of Florida and Wayne State University found that older Americans who suffer from any type of stress in their lives used prayer to ward it off. In addition, nurse researchers found that prayer is the most frequently reported alternative treatment used by seniors to feel better or maintain health in general (*Science Daily,* Jan., 2001*).*

University of Florida College of Nursing Associate Professor Ann L. Horgas and Wayne State University doctoral student Karen S. Dunn reported that 96 percent of older adults use prayer to specifically cope with stress.

Their study, published in the December issue of the *Journal of Holistic Nursing*, also shows that 84 percent of the respondents reported using prayer more than other alternative remedies to feel better or maintain their health. In fact, from a list of 32 alternative therapies, prayer was used more often than exercise, heat, relaxation techniques, humor, or herbal remedies to maintain overall health (*Science Daily*, Jan., 2001). Again, I repeat, "prayer is the foundation of everything that we do." It is very important for prevention and reversal of diseases.

"There's been recent research showing that most Americans pray and that prayer has a positive effect on mental and physical health," said Horgas. She said that most of the studies about prayer and health have been conducted on very ill, hospitalized, or surgical patients (*Science Daily*, Jan., 2001). Nurse Horgas and Dunn interviewed 50 people—average age 74—at six community senior centers, and one church in Detroit. Seventy percent of the respondents were women, of which 52 percent were African American and 48 percent were Caucasian. About half of the respondents were Catholic (48 percent), followed by Protestants (46 percent), and the remainder was classified as other. They determined that African Americans reported their use of prayer to cope with stress significantly more than Caucasians. The study concluded that prayer could improve health.

Other studies, such as one conducted with women at an in vitro fertilization (IVF) clinic concluded that healing occurred at a higher rate when total strangers prayed for them. Another study found that people who are in prayer groups have fewer complications after undergoing risky cardiovascular surgery.

After surveying more than 2,000 adults, Harvard University Researchers discovered that people who are grappling with chronic, tough-to-treat health conditions such as back pain and arthritis find a conversation with God to be more helpful than a visit with the doctor. Survey results follow:

PRAYER -OR- THE DOCTOR		
Health Condition	Prayer	Doctor
Severe Depression	68%	48%
Anxiety	70%	38%
Arthritis	60%	40%
Back Pain	59%	30%
Cancer	81%	78%

As with other illnesses, stress can also affect the physical and emotional aspects of the human body. It can shut down the immune and digestive systems, which are two major systems in the body. Nevertheless, prayer helps to restore health to the body. It is a primary component of healing that has been tested and proven by various universities. Researchers call prayer working in "mysterious ways." Actually, it is not mysterious; it is divine intervention by God.

FOREWORD

In this volume, I will discuss some foods, condiments, and appliances that society introduced to our grandparents and our parents; which we have now introduced to our children, grandchildren, and great-grandchildren.

Please read this information carefully. I am sharing this information with you because in order to live a long quality life, you must take care of your God-given temple. If you want to live a long quality life, free of adverse health conditions, pay attention to this information and free yourself from the bondage of slavery to these foods.

YOU CAN DO IT! Remember, *"With God, all things are possible"* (Mark 9:23). The Bible says in Proverbs 3:7 and 8, *"Be not wise in thine own eyes; fear the Lord and depart from evil. It shall be health to thy navel, and marrow to thy bones."*

MESSAGE FROM THE FOUNDER

Hosea 4:6 says, "*Our people are dying for lack of knowledge.*" Therefore, it is critically-important that we take responsibility for our bodies. We need to have knowledge, godly wisdom, and counsel on honing this body temple, caring for it, and creating a lifestyle that glorifies God. Psalm 139:14 says, "*... we were fearfully and wonderfully made; marvelous are thy works.*" As we grow to fully understand the human body, the wonderful work of God's hand, and that we are formed in his image and likeness; we will then seek to bring our bodies into subjection. The body will be regarded as

James A. Dail, Sr.
PhD, ThD, ND

the wonderful structure it is, formed by God and given to us to take steward and charge over it and to be kept in harmonious action.

In our Christian teachings, we are told about honoring and glorifying the body as far as avoiding adultery, fornication, lusts of the flesh, etc. It is unfortunate that all too often, the importance of nutrition, a healthy lifestyle—proper eating, rest, and exercise—are left out of the teachings. Thessalonians 5:23 lets us to know that God wants our whole spirit, soul, and body to be preserved blameless unto the coming of our Lord Jesus Christ.

First Corinthians 6:19 and 20 tells us that our bodies are not our own to treat as we please, to cripple by habits that lead to decay, making it impossible to render to God perfect service. We were bought with a price, and our lives and all our faculties belong to Him. He is caring for us every moment. He keeps the living machinery in action. If we were left to run it for one moment, we would die. It is through Him that we live, breathe, and have our being. We are absolutely dependent on God. Our soul, body, and spirit are His.

God gave His only begotten Son for the body as well as the soul. Our entire life belongs to Him to be consecrated to His service so that we may glorify Him through exercising every faculty He has given us.

The wonderful mechanism of the human body does not receive half of the care that is so often given to materials such as our automobiles. We are willing to spend extra money to put high-grade fuel in them; but, yet we put all kinds of destructive trash in our bodies that we have the nerve to call food. These "things" that we ingest break the body and mind down, cause it to dysfunction, creating sickness, diseases, and untimely death.

We have an obligation to God to present Him with clean, pure, and healthy bodies. When we choose the Will of God and are conformed to the character of Christ, the Spirit can act through our organs and faculties. The Spirit of Christ is to take possession of the organs of speech, mental powers, physical and moral powers.

Many times, we argue that we can do destructive things to our bodies because "we have to die from something." Therefore, we try to justify destructive eating habits and lifestyles. We try to justify eating Twinkies, swine, and all manners of pork, processed foods, sugars, and on and on—things of the world. First John 2:15 and 16 instructs us to "*Love not the world, neither the things that are in the world. If any man love the world, the love of the father is not in Him. For all that is in the world, the lust of the flesh, and the lust of the eyes, and the pride of life, is not of the Father, but of the world.*" In Genesis 1:29 and 30, it says, "*And the Lord said, 'Behold, I have given you every herb bearing seed, which is upon the face of all the earth, and every tree, in the which is the fruit of a tree yielding seed; to you it shall be for meat.'* "

We must be diligent in our conviction, without excuse, to honor His temple. It is not unlawful to go out and eat a hamburger. However, by eating it, you will suffer the consequences of the fat, the salt, and the blood it contains. First Corinthians 6:12 states, "*Everything is permissible for me; but not everything is beneficial. Everything is permissible for me, but I will not be mastered by anything.*" Are you a slave to your appetite? One of the ploys of the devil is reflected in how deadly foods are manufactured to be pleasing to the eye through packaging, preservatives, flavor enhancers, and food colorings.

We must take victory over appetite and learn how to select our food and prepare it God's way. Jesus died that we may have life and have it abundantly. This includes abundant health. Salvation means good health, spirit, soul, and body. Good nutrition does not mean depriving yourself of foods that taste good. We need to enjoy the foods we eat.

Wholeness and holy is a journey. Now, 1 Thessalonians 5:23 reads, "*And the very God of peace sanctify you holy.*" Paul was giving his final exaltation to the church of Thessonica when he told the brothers there what they needed to do and how they needed to preserve their existence and the wholeness in their lives. "*And Paul said, 'I pray God your whole spirit and soul and body be preserved blameless upon the coming of our Lord Jesus Christ.' *" See folks, in this passage of scripture, "blameless" means without defect. Romans 12:1 reads, "*I beseech you, therefore, brothers by the mercies of God, that you present your bodies a living sacrifice, holy and acceptable to God as your reasonable service.*" Now, without what? Blemish, because Paul knew that God would not accept anything that is sacrificed to Him with blemishes. Everything that is sacrificed to God has to be whole. "Whole" means without defect. The devil's job is to convince you to do ungodly things so that your lifestyle or life will not exact wholeness. Therefore, if you do not have wholeness, then you are not seeking holiness. Paul says in Romans 12:2, "*And be not conformed to this world, but be ye transformed to renewing of your mind that you may prove what is that good and acceptable and perfect will of God.*"

If we look at Romans 10:13, we will see that it tells us what the Christian church is based upon—the fiber of the Christian church is taught that, "*Whosoever shall call upon the Name of the Lord shall be saved.*" Jesus died for our salvation. We all know that, right? "Salvation" means saved, right? According to Strong's number 4982 and Romans 10:13, saved means "To save, to keep safe and sound, to rescue from danger or destruction, from injury or peril, to save a suffering one, from diseases, to make well ill, restore the health, to make whole, to heal the whole body." So now, are you saved? But now, in the book of Matthew, Jesus says, "**Heaven is at hand, heaven** *is within you*." God knew that without heaven in you on earth, there is no way that you can do His perfect Will. You need a body to do God's Will.

TOOLS FOR HEALTH AND HEALING GOD'S WAY

Truth & Knowledge
Vol. 1

EVERYDAY POISONS

Salt

Let us look at salt. Salt in the form of sodium chloride is a deadly, poisonous, and addictive drug. It is possibly the greatest killer of humanity. For years, the medical profession told us that it was necessary to take additional salt or salt tablets into our bodies during hot weather when the body is sweating excessively. It is our stand that this is one of the biggest mistakes ever. Why is it that when we have heart problems or diabetes, the first thing the doctor does is to have us remove salt from our diets? Even the idiopathic practitioners know and understand the dangers of sodium chloride in our bodies. If they tell you to cut back on salt when you are sick, do you not think that salt contributes to your condition? Instead of cutting back, you should just cut it out. Salt, without adding water can lead to death.

Salt in the form of sodium chloride dehydrates the body. We do not want to get "sodium" mixed up with "sodium chloride" because

they are two different chemicals. When sodium chloride enters the body, it draws water from the blood stream causing the body to send out an SOS signal that manifests itself as thirst. Now, think about it! When you eat a bowl of soup, especially canned soup, which is 90 to 95 percent water, the body sends a signal to the brain, PLEASE SEND WATER! Remember now, if you are drinking soup, which is predominantly water, then why is your body sending that signal to your brain? Water helps dilute the salt concentration in order to help neutralize its poisoning of the body. Salt really poisons the body when you consume it.

Most people, of course, consume too much salt. Any salt is too much. Salt is found in every commercial food product. Studies have found that even fresh meat in the grocery stores has been infused with sodium chloride. Yes, the good, old bloody-looking meat in your favorite store is infused with at least 500 milligrams of sodium chloride per four ounces (for preservative). This is what they call 'fresh meat!' I am not talking about the canned meat. The grocer is adding sodium chloride to the fresh meat and you add more salt to it when you cook it. Think about this! If there are 500 milligrams per four ounces and most people eat a whole pound of meat in one sitting, then a pound of meat (16 ounces) would contain four times 500 (or 2,000) milligrams of sodium chloride (salt) even before you add your own salt to it. Therefore, you can see how deadly the meat can be, both before and after you prepare it. An example of what salt does to the body is exhibited when a person goes on a fast. It is very common for them to lose 10 pounds or more in just a few days.

Unfortunately, many people on dialysis do not drink a lot of liquid because they try to minimize the amount flowing through their urinary tract. However, they continue to eat foods filled with sodium chloride, which means their bodies are being poisoned with no outlet. They are not consuming enough fluid to dilute that salt in order to slow down the poisonous effect on the body. That is why the health of people on dialysis begins to deteriorate at a rapid rate. We will discuss more about dialysis further in the book.

Salt found throughout the body can cause unbelievable harm. Some of the physical problems caused by salt are hardening of the arteries, arthritis, ulcers, distorted vision, blindness, high blood pressure, tumors, cancers, and a multitude of other degenerative disorders. Remember, salt is an antibiotic—it kills life. So how can we expect to live while eating what kills life? Salt is used as a preservative because it kills bacteria. Bacterium is life and salt kills life.

Salt begins as an addictive influence in the lives of little children when their parents cook all the flavor and nutrients out of the food, then add salt in an effort to make it taste better. We start our children on that dangerous journey to premature death and a lot of pain and suffering by adding it to their food when they are very young.

Remember, when we abuse different substances and different foods, we can count on receiving a payday eventually, because of the irreversible law, which says, *"Be not deceived, God is not mocked"* (Galatians 6:7a).

Milk

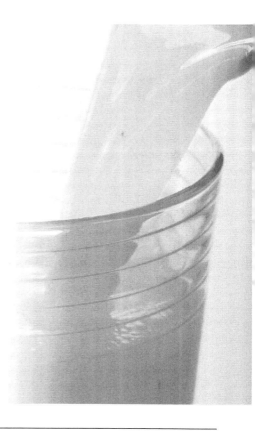

"Dairy is no longer recommended or required," says the Physicians Committee for Responsible Medicine (PCRM). This information is also based on a cancer report. Dairy products including milk, ice cream, cheese, and yogurt, are major causes of a host of degenerative diseases including, but not limited to, osteoporosis (weak bones), cardiovascular disease, Attention Deficit Disorder (ADD), Attention Deficit Hyperactivity Disorder (ADHD), autism, cancer, vitamin D toxicity, diabetes, and a host of other diseases. Galatians 6:7b tells us *"For whatsoever a man soweth, he shall also reap"*

This even applies to what we put into our mouths.

Milk and Osteoporosis

Dairy products offer a false sense of security to those concerned about osteoporosis. In countries where dairy products are not generally consumed, there are fewer cases of osteoporosis compared to those in the US. The US consumes more dairy compared to other countries worldwide.

The University of Harvard Nurses' Health Study followed 7,800 women for a 12-year period and found that milk, dairy, cheese, yogurt, and ice cream did not protect against bone fractures. They found that the who drank three glasses of milk per day had more bone fractures than the women who rarely drank milk at all. In African areas where no one drinks milk, there is no such thing as osteoporosis or weak bones. Why? Because they consume a plant-based diet. They get their calcium from plants, the same way we need to get our source of calcium.

Dairy Products and Diabetes

Diabetes is a major epidemic within the church. One of the factors is our consumption of dairy. The more dairy one consumes, the greater the risk of developing diabetes. Currently, more than 60 percent of adult churchgoers have diabetes or are pre-diabetes. At a minimum, several reports based on the PCRM linked insulin-dependent diabetes to specific protein in dairy products. This form of diabetes begins in childhood and leads to blindness. It contributes to heart disease, kidney damage, and amputations because of poor circulation.

These medical conditions result from the use of your so-called "dairy." Studies of various countries show a strong correlation between the use of dairy products and the incidence of diabetes. A recent report in the *New England Journal of Medicine* adds substantial support to the long-standing theory that cow's milk protein stimulates the production of antibodies, which, in turn destroys the insulin-producing pancreatic cells.

The pancreas produces the insulin we need to move the sugar out of the blood stream and into our cells; while milk causes the gradual destruction of the pancreatic cells, especially after an infection. This causes the cellular protein to be exposed to the damage of antibodies. Diabetes becomes evident when 80-90 percent of the insulin-producing beta cells are destroyed. Milk protein is also among the most common causes of food allergies. Many children with food allergies can only consume one or two different types of food. Removing dairy from their diet corrects food allergy problems.

Cardiovascular Disease and Milk

The consumption of dairy also leads to cardiovascular disease. Early signs of heart disease in American teenagers have been documented. While children do need a certain amount of fat in their diets, there is no nutritional requirement for cow's milk fat. On the contrary, cow's milk is high in saturated fat but low in essential fatty acid, which contributes to major heart disease. Heart disease does not start when we are 40 years old, but rather when our parents begin to feed us cow's milk and cheese. We may not realize that cheese is 10 times worse than milk, because it takes 10 pounds of milk to make 1 pound of cheese.

Research has shown that dairy is a cause of many different forms of cancers including breast, prostate, colon, stomach, and cervical. A Florida researcher, Dr. Robert Cade and his colleagues have identified a milk protein, casomorphin, as the probable cause of attention deficit disorder and autism. They have found that there is high concentration of beta-casomorphin-7 in the blood and urine in patients with either schizophrenia or autism (*Autism 1999*, 3). We are putting our children on Ritalin, when all we have to do is remove milk and milk products from their diets.

Reports have shown that milk may very well be the major factor in children with autism. One out of five American children has been diagnosed with ADD, and one out of five takes Ritalin. An alternative therapy is to remove dairy from your children's diet. Regardless of what you have heard through advertisements, read in your health books, or heard from your doctors; there is scientific research to prove the dangers of dairy products. (*For further research, go to www.notmilk.com for a host of different problems associated with dairy*).

Sugar

What about sugar? There are many things sugar does to the body. For example, it depletes the body's supply of biotin, which is a main mineral needed in our body for health and wellness. It also depletes the choline, and Vitamin B-1, which is our energy vitamin.

Sugar in the form of "sucrose"—the white refined sugar—decreases the sharpness or the mental acuity of the mind. Our so-called table sugar is a product that is made by man. Man isolated sugar from God's plants where sugar grows naturally, and turned it into a physically and mentally addictive drug. Sugar is released very quickly in the blood stream just like alcohol. Alcohol is 90 percent sugar and has a toxic, poisoning, drug effect on the body. It ferments in the body, causing the formation of carbonic acid and alcohol. The acid is very destructive to the cells in the body. It literally burns the cells, leading to a paralyzing effect on the nerves. Sugar turns into alcohol in your intestines. Just as alcohol can cause violent actions, sugar also can cause violent actions. It has damaging effects on the kidneys, the nerves, and brain function—especially the concentration, observation, and locomotion of the brain.

Sucrose interferes with the transport of Vitamin C in the body.

Vitamin C is an antioxidant that protects us from cell damage caused by free radicals. So what little Vitamin C we do consume in the foods we eat is disrupted when we eat sugar. Sugar will stop Vitamin C from being absorbed throughout the body.

We do not want to get sucrose confused with "glucose," which is a sugar the body needs to function and keep our minds sharp. We must also understand that sucrose and sugar mean the same thing. Sucrose accelerates the aging process. Studies have shown that people who consume a lot of sugar age more rapidly than folks who do not.

Sucrose increases blood pressure and is one of the causes of Crohn's disease—inflammation of the bowels. It causes gallstones and kidney stones. It irritates the stomach and suppresses the immune system. Of course, suppressing the immune system reduces the production of antibodies—our army that God put in us to protect us from enemies like different viruses and different bacteria. We need our antibodies! It also increases the risk of colon cancer and breast cancer, and increases free radicals, which is a major cause of obesity. In addition, sugar and caffeine cause the liver to produce more cholesterol. That is one reason why the concentration of cholesterol is so high in our bodies. It also causes the body to produce an excessive amount of insulin, which leads to diabetes.

Other effects include increased secretion of calcium that is flushed out of our bodies. We know how important calcium is for strong bones and teeth and the generation and health of the cells in our bodies. It also increases urinary chromium excretions. Chromium regulates the sugar in our bodies. In addition, it interferes with the absorption of magnesium and causes the depletion of the body's phosphorus. Often, what we will do is alternate from sugar or sucrose to fructose, thinking that fructose will be healthier since it comes from fruits. On the contrary, it is the same thing. In fact, fructose accelerates the aging process faster than sucrose.

A high concentration of sugar in the blood causes diabetes and hypoglycemia. Some of the symptoms of hypoglycemia are headaches and irritability. Remember, sugar causes irritability, depression, fatigue, and an inability to concentrate. It also causes frustration and anger for no apparent reason, similar to the effects of alcohol.

Actually, some marriage counselors familiar with hypoglycemia estimate that up to 50 percent of all marriage problems can be traced to this condition. Sugar destroys calcium, shatters the nervous system, and causes tooth decay, hair loss, senility, circulation problems, heart problems and a host of other health issues.

In his book, *The Golden 7 Plus 1*, page 102, Dr. C. Samuel West states, "If you fail to do something about your simple sugar intake beginning today, you will be committing willful suicide; and that is a fact when it comes to sugar."

Why Not Meat?

I know you are guessing I will tell you that meat is bad for you. Well, I am. Moreover, I am sure you are going to ask, "Well, what can I eat?" My answer would be to eat what Daniel ate—a diet that follows the principals of God. Be obedient to the Word of God. If you are obedient to the Word of God, you are going to eat what God says. God constructed your body. He knows exactly what you

need to fuel it and to keep it healthy. That is why He gave us fruits, vegetables, nuts, and grains. You know that it is a challenge for most people to change from a carnivore's diet to a diet of living—consisting of fresh, nutritional foods. Eating healthy is much easier than you might think. There are literally thousands of highly-nutritious foods and tasty dishes, as you will read in this book, that contain things like grains, millet, quinoa, buckwheat, groats, garbanzo beans, lentils, brown rice and tofu, just to name a few.

We highly suggest learning to cook vegetarian dishes. They are actually very easy to prepare. Just make your normal dishes without adding meats. Many times people say they have to add meat for flavor, but you do not need to do that. If you drink the juice, you might as well eat the berry. Therefore, in flavoring food with meat, you might as well eat the meat. You have to understand that all the impurities and all the things that are in the meat are cooking into the broth.

We at Reformation Healing Ministries International really do not like the terms vegetarian or vegan. We like to use the term PETEGAT, which means "Persons Eating to Edify God's Amazing Temple." Many so-called world vegetarians are not that healthy because they eat sugar and many other types of foods that affect the body adversely. Just because a food came from a plant does not necessarily mean it is healthy. There are many plant-based foods that are perverted through chemical processing. For example, white rice, according to a vegan or vegetarian may be great. However, eating white rice can cause diabetes and cancer, weaken the immune system, and increases the chance of getting a whole host of other diseases. We, at Reformation Healing Ministries International teach you how to be PETEGAT eaters. Everything we teach is based on PETEGAT, not vegetarian or vegan. It just so happens that in order to have a perfect diet, we need to use plant-based foods. Remember, we came from the dirt, so does it not make common sense to eat the food that comes from the dirt?

So far, we have discussed how salt, dairy, and meat are not good for us. Later, we will give you a list of foods to replace those things— foods that will edify and build the sanctuary of God and protect

God's house (your body)—so that you can maximize the potential that God has put in your life and in the lives of those in your area of influence.

Coca Cola Soft Drinks

Let us discuss Coke. You may not know it, but in many states within the US, the highway patrol carries two gallons of Coke in the trunk of their cruisers to remove blood from the highway after a car accident.

Following are just a few uses of Coca Cola:
- You can put a T-bone steak in a bowl of Coke and it will be gone in two days.
- You can clean a toilet bowl by pouring a can of Coke into it, let it set for one hour, and then flush clean.
- The citric acid in Coke removes stains from vitreous china.
- Remove rust spots from chrome car bumpers by rubbing the bumper with a rumpled up piece of aluminum foil dipped in Coca-Cola.
- Clean corrosion from a car's battery terminals by pouring a can of Coca-Cola over the terminals to bubble away the corrosion.
- Apply a cloth soaked in Coca-Cola to remove rust from a bolt.

- To bake a moist ham, some say you should empty a can or two of Coke into the baking pan, wrap the ham in aluminum foil, and bake. Thirty minutes before the ham is finished, remove the foil, allow the dripping to mix with the Coke for sumptuous brown gravy. Think about it—there are three things wrong with this scenario. First, aluminum foil causes neurological problems. It affects the brain cells and the nerves of the human body. Secondly, there are nitrates in ham that cause cancer, cardiovascular disease, and a host of other diseases. Thirdly, the Benzopyrene and HCA's in the ham are the same things that we find in cigarette smoke that cause cancer. Ham, along with the Coke, is a recipe for diseases.

- Loosen grease stains by emptying a can of Coke into a load of greasy clothes, add detergent, and run through a regular cycle.
- Coke will also clean road haze from your windshield.
- The active ingredient in Coke is phosphoric acid. Its PH is 2.8. It will dissolve a nail in about four days. Phosphorus acid also leeches calcium from bones and is a major contributor to the rise in osteoporosis.
- A commercial truck must use a hazardous material placard card reserved for highly corrosive materials in order to carry Coca-Cola syrup or the concentrate.
- The distributors of Coke have been using it to clean the engines of their trucks for more than 20 years.

This information is about Coca-Cola, but all soft drinks have some of the same ingredients. This is just some information you can use. If these drinks can be used for such diverse and destructive reasons, how much more destruction will they do to our bodies?

Gatorade: The Truth Behind the Product

Gatorade is classified as a non-carbonated, nutrient-enhanced drink. Many believe it is a harmless drink that we often times feed to our children during their sports game to increase their electrolytes.

We often think that if the government approves or advertises something, then it can never be harmful to us. The government is in the world system and will allow anything to be produced and used by all the citizens just so that they can gain from the excess taxes. The more revenue the manufacturers generate, the more taxes are being paid to the government. Our health is not the government's priority. Remember that the Food and Drug Administration (FDA) is the chief devil of this country. They only approve things that will cause diseases in the body. Everything that the FDA approves has a major side effect. We rely on our government to give us instructions on what we need to do to our bodies. What we really need to do is always refer to the Word of God on what we need to eat and drink. God made "good ole water" for us; but then man said that we need additional electrolytes, which is a LIE. If that was the case, God would have thought of that in the beginning. God did not see fit to add electrolytes in our water. Water has all the electrolytes that the body needs for health.

If you reflect back in the old days before Gatorade, many of the athletes were not wrapped up in different bandages as they are today. Jesse Owens and all the other athletes who broke all types of world records in sports did not have to worry about electrolytes or using Gatorade. The University of Florida created Gatorade in 1965 to make money off a drink that they claimed to increase electrolytes in the body and prevent dehydration. All we need is good old H2O to keep us from dehydrating. Unfortunately, many people now rely on that poison.

Examining the Ingredients in Gatorade

The ingredients in Gatorade include water, sucrose syrup, glucose-fructose syrup, citric acid, natural flavors, sodium chloride (salt), sodium citrate, monopotassium phosphate, estergum, and sunflower oil. The colorings include FD&C Red 40, Blue 1, and Yellow 5.

1) FD&C Yellow 5, also known as tartrazine, is a synthetic yellow-orange coloring agent derived from cold tar found in Gatorade. The toxic effects include attention deficit disorder, asthma, hives, thyroid tumors, lymphocyctic lymphomas, chromosome damage, and allergies. By law, the FDA was designed to safeguard our food; yet, this coloring is still being approved.

2) The use of FD&C Blue 1 may cause bronco constriction, eosinophilotactic response, and chromosomal damage, which increases aging.

3) According to research on food colorings from the American Academy of Pediatric Committee on Drugs, FD&C Red 40 causes tumors/lymphomas, severe temper tantrums, and headaches. Moreover, we wonder why our children suffer from ADHD and other diseases. The FDA approved a list of food coloring for use in the US in 2000. The source of the health problems is certain ingredients in foods and drinks.

4) Sodium Chloride in Gatorade causes the excretion of calcium from the body. For example, every additional 1000mg of salt in the diet causes the excretion of 500mg of calcium. The more salt that you take in, the more calcium leaves the body. The USDA recommends that we use no more than 2000mg of sodium a day. Sodium chloride also causes hardening of the arteries, promotes hypertension (high blood pressure), and edema.

5) Sodium Citrate in Gatorade causes confusion, convulsion (seizure), dizziness, high blood pressure, irritability, mood changes, muscle pain, twitching, slow breathing, unexplained anxiety, weakness, difficulty breathing, and swelling of the lower legs. The toxicology may act as an irritant.

6) Sucrose causes the depletion of biotin, phosphorous and vitamin B. It also causes gallstones and kidney stones, interferes with the transport of Vitamin C through the body, it accelerates the aging process, increases blood pressure and cholesterol, irritates the stomach, suppresses the immune system, and reduces the antibodies in the body. Individuals who consume the sucrose in Gatorade have an increased risk for breast and colon cancer as well as a rise in blood sugar level and insulin production. Other complications include tooth decay and the interference of the absorption of magnesium.

7) Fructose accelerates the aging process and the premature breakdown of the cells faster than sucrose.

8) Monopotassium Phosphate may cause irritation of the eye, respiratory track, and skin.

These are some of the complications from the ingredients in Gatorade. You can just think about all the other approved products that are very unhealthy for the body. Many athletes are getting paid millions of dollars to advertise Gatorade. They are playing a game they enjoy but they are aggressive. They fight and are always ready for confrontation. We often times wonder why our children are so aggressive. This is because we are giving them drinks like Gatorade. We cannot depend on the world to make sure that we are healthy. We also count on the church to help promote health and wellness in order to get rid of the many types of diseases plaguing our communities.

Sucralose/Aspartame—A Poison Used to Replace A Poison

"Sucralose," which is the same as Splenda, is believed by many to be a healthy alternative to refined sucrose (table sugar), when in all actuality, it is much worse. This particular section of the book discusses how some things that we replace as alternative food additives and condiment such as sugar, salt, and others, can be even more dangerous to our health. Replacing sucrose with another form of sweetener is the way that the devil can make things appear to be healthy by deceiving us to believe it is good for us, when they are much more harmful than the original condiment. Artificial sweeteners are found in 95 percent of sugarless foods, drinks, gum, and vitamins.

Many individuals replace their need to sweeten their foods and beverages with the artificial sweetener known as "Aspartame." The brand name for Aspartame is Equal, Equal Measure, and NutraSweet. It can even be in foods and vitamins such as Flintstones vitamins for children. Controversy surrounding Aspartame has arisen due to possible health risks. Research shows that Aspartame is a major cause of many diseases.

The Toxic Effect of Aspartame

Aspartame causes tachycardia (heart problem). Research has shown that there are many complications and diseases resulting from the use of Aspartame. It causes brain cancer, systemic lupus, and erythematosus lupus. Its toxicity really mimics lupus. In addition, it also leads to diabetes, fatigue, male impotence, asthma, Alzheimer's, epilepsy, Parkinson's disease, Graves' disease, joint pain, anxiety, convulsions, deafness, depression, headaches, insomnia, and irritability. Research even goes on to show that the use of Aspartame can cause memory impairment, migraines, multiple sclerosis, nausea, neuralgia, neuritis, neuropathy, numbness, optic nerve damage, vertigo, loss of taste and even speech impairment.

Aspartame is extremely harmful to the body. This poison is found in candy and vitamins that are given to children. Many foods that manufacturers claim to be sugar-free actually contain Aspartame as an ingredient. Remember not to fall for the tricks of the devil. Do natural sweeteners like Stevia, fruits, and vegetables like raisins and dates, or even a little maple syrup or raw honey. Remember, too much of a good thing is not healthy.

Coffee

If America or the church has a national drink, it would be coffee. Americans, especially the churchgoers, drink coffee with breakfast, in meetings, when they are traveling, and they even have coffee breaks. The devil has influenced man to create a pastime that is destroying the sanctuary of God.

Starbucks is one of the fastest-growing coffee shops. Dunkin Donuts and every place that you go sells coffee. Satan has really acquired victory by using this weapon against the body of Christ.

Americans consume more than two billion pounds of coffee each year. Coffee drinking is viewed as innocent and harmless. It is a natural occurrence to get a cup of coffee. Many people say that nothing is wrong with coffee and that coffee is something that everyone drinks. Remember that everybody was doing wrong on the earth and God destroyed the earth except for Noah and his family. If everyone does wrong, then the wrath will be against everyone who is

doing wrong.

Coffee is a poison to the sanctuary of God. Most people do not realize that coffee is a drug. If you do not think coffee is a drug, then try to stop drinking it. Nothing that God placed on the earth will have you dependent on it based on the whims of your flesh. If coffee was something that we needed for health and to edify God's amazing temple, then we would not need to talk about all the harms of coffee. Remember that God loves you, and He would not have you consume something that would destroy His sanctuary because He owns your body. God needs your body as much as you need God. He cannot do His Will on earth without your body; and Satan knows this information. Satan influenced man to create an environment that seems harmless, when in fact; it is detrimental to your overall health.

Coffee is a Harmful Drug

Coffee is not a food and has no important nutrients. The only effect it has on the body is to destroy the cells and prematurely age the body. How in the world can God sanction something that is so destructive?

Coffee is a drug. It has a high level of caffeine along with harmful oils and other toxic substances. Caffeine is the main ingredient and problem in coffee. It is a stimulant that excites the nerves in the body into unusual and injurious activity as it is trying to expel caffeine. This poison is not supposed to be in the body.

The main function of the immune system is to protect us. The immune system goes into defense when you drink coffee. It gives a sensation of exhilaration and after-effects including mental depression, decreased muscular power, and damages to the liver and kidney. When caffeine first enters the body, the blood pressure increases, and the heart beats more forcefully. As the drug is expelled from the body, the heart beats with less force and the blood pressure falls below normal. If coffee is good for you, why then does it raise the blood pressure when you first drink it, and then lower the blood pressure when it leaves the body? That is an indication that coffee is not good.

Caffeine causes the kidneys to work overtime in an effort to expel the caffeine poison. As coffee drinking continues, the kidneys weaken and become less efficient. Degeneration of the kidneys is the result. Many people are on dialysis because they drink several cups of coffee a day.

Oils in Coffee

Coffee contains a volatile oil, which irritates the lining of the stomach and intestines. This irritation causes frequent urination, ulcers, gastritis, spontaneous abortions, stillbirths, premature births, and a host of other problems. In fact, if coffee can cause miscarriages, then it is doing something very negative to the body. If it causes you to abort a child that God has blessed in the womb, then you know that the devil is doing his work and doing it very effectively.

In a study in the *American Journal of Obstetrics and Gynecology*, Kaiser Permanente researchers analyzed information about caffeine drinking by 1,063 women early in their pregnancies. Their research showed that women drinking less than 200 milligrams of caffeine a day (about two cups of regular coffee or five cans of caffeinated soda) were 40 percent more likely to miscarry than women who said they drank no caffeinated beverages. Those who drank 200 milligrams or more of caffeine per day had about twice the miscarriage risk as women who drank none. This report, written by Dr. De-Kun Li, concluded that pregnant women should avoid all caffeinated drinks.

Caffeine is not good for the body. Research from John Hopkins University recommends the use of green tea as an alternative. It is best to avoid coffee, caffeine, and chocolate. We need to be careful with what we drink in order to avoid certain diseases.

The poisonous effect of coffee on the body works slowly. The devil is very patient in what he does. Most coffee drinkers do not realize that their habit is slowing destroying parts of their body. Remember that coffee is not a food but is an addictive, poisonous drug that can do great harm to the body. It is not capable of doing anything good.

Unfortunately, a lot of research reveals that coffee has healthy proprieties and is good for you. We need to realize that something that will tear the body down and can possibly cause suffering of diseases and premature death is not beneficial to our health. The key is to leave coffee alone.

Microwave Cooking

Microwave cooking is one of the most devastating causes of ill health. It is certainly one of the most ignored. There was a lawsuit in 1991 in Oklahoma where a woman named Norma Levitt had hip surgery, but was killed by a simple blood transfusion when a nurse warmed the blood for the transfusion in a microwave oven. Now think about that. If microwaving is a healthy thing to do, then the microwaved blood would not have had an adverse effect on the health of this young lady. Transfusion blood is routinely warmed, but not in microwave ovens. Does it not therefore follow that microwave cooking does something quite different from just warming up the food?

The University of Minnesota, in a radio announcement, gave a little evidence of the harm caused by microwave cooking. This is what the announcement read, "Microwaves are not recommended for heating a baby's bottle. The bottle may seem cool to the touch, but the liquid inside may become extremely hot and can burn the baby's mouth and throat."

Heating the bottle in a microwave can also cause slight changes in the milk. In infant formula, there may be a loss of some vitamins.

In breast milk, some protective properties like the micronutrients and antibodies can be destroyed. Therefore, DO NOT MICROWAVE BABY'S FORMULA OR BREAST MILK. Instead, warm the bottle by holding it under tap water or by setting it in a bowl of warm water and then testing it on your wrist before feeding. It may take a few minutes longer; but it is much safer.

Two researchers, Blanc, who worked as a food scientist and Hertel of the Swiss Federal Institute of Biochemistry and the University Institute for Biochemistry confirmed that microwave cooking significantly changes food nutrients. They studied the effect that microwave food had on individuals by taking blood samples immediately after eating. They found that after eating microwaved food, hemoglobin levels decreased. These results showed anemic tendencies. The situation became even more pronounced during the second month of the study. Subsequently, it revealed that many people are anemic because they microwave their food. If these results were obtained only after a couple of months, then think about what would happen if they conducted the same study after years of microwave use. Much of our illnesses can be avoided if we refrain from using microwaves.

The violent change that microwaving causes to the food molecules forms new life forms called radiolytic compounds. These mutations are unknown in the natural world. People do not even know what those mutations are. Ordinary cooking can also cause the formation of radiolytic compounds, which is no doubt, one reason why it is better to eat plenty of raw food. Microwave cooking causes a much greater number, causing deterioration in your blood and immune system. In addition, the number of lymphocytes increases after eating microwaved food. Hematologists (those who study blood) take this very seriously; because this is often a sign of highly, harmful effects such as poison. In other words, "it is poisonous."

Cholesterol levels also increase after eating microwaved food. The liver produces more cholesterol due to the stress that the microwave food causes your system. Blanc and Hertel found that eating microwaved food increases cholesterol and white blood cells, decreases red blood cells, and causes production of radiolytic compounds

(compounds unknown in nature).

Russia also conducted its own research on the use of microwave ovens, and ultimately placed a ban on its use. The ban was lifted in 1976. Researchers found that heating meat in the microwave produces cancer-causing agents. It causes cancer agents in milk and cereal grains. In this research, cancer-causing free radicals were formed in the minerals and molecules in the plant substance. They also found that although fruits and vegetables do not contain cholesterol, if microwaved, the level of cholesterol in the body increases. Of course, there are many research studies conducted throughout the world that confirm that microwave eating and microwave heating of food is of great detriment to our health. In fact, if you can bring water to a boil in a microwave, let it cool to room temperature, and pour it over your plants; it will cause your plant to wilt. It can actually kill or destroy your plant. Plants are live organisms, as is your body. Therefore, microwave use would do the same thing to your body as it would do to those plants. A lot of diseases and death are in the world because of microwave cooking.

*   *   *   *   *   *

PROGRAM TO WELLNESS

Water

Water is the major component to life. Between 90 and 95 percent of people who have headaches are dehydrated. Therefore, water is the most important medicine that we need to combat many diseases. Many times, we have issues in our bodies just because we do not drink enough water. We try to substitute it with drinks like coffee, tea, Kool-Aid, Gatorade, and other things. Research reports the following:

- Seventy-five percent of Americans are chronically dehydrated.
- Thirty seven percent of Americans' thirst mechanism is so weak that it is often mistaken for hunger.
- Mild dehydration will slow down one's metabolism as much as 3 percent.
- A study conducted by The University of Washington showed that one glass of water could shut down midnight hunger pains 100 percent of the time.
- The lack of water is the number one trigger of daytime fatigue. When we are fatigued, we drink everything except water. We drink Coke, tea, or coffee. We drink all the things that dehydrate the body versus things that are going to re-hydrate the body. Preliminary research indicates that we should drink at least one-half ounce of water per pound of body weight. For example, if you weigh 200 pounds, you need 100 ounces of water per day. You should not drink it all at one time. You should sip it,

not guzzle it down. For example, you should drink a maximum of five ounces of water every 30 minutes, because the kidneys cannot process more than that amount in an hour's time-frame. Drinking the right amount of water per day for your body weight can also significantly ease back or joint pain for up to 80 percent of sufferers. Dehydration is a cause of joint and back pain.

- A mere two percent drop in body water can trigger fuzziness, short-term memory, trouble with basic math, and difficulty focusing on a computer screen or on a printed page. Many of our children are having problems in school because their brains are dehydrated. The brain is made up of 75 to 80 percent water.

- Drinking at least five glasses of water daily decreases the risk of colon cancer by 45 percent. It also slashes the risk of breast cancer by 79 percent and bladder cancer by 50 percent.

- Water:
    - helps carry nutrients and oxygen to the cells of your body,
    - moistens oxygen for breathing,
    - helps convert food into energy,
    - protects and cushions vital organs,
    - helps the body absorb nutrients,
    - counts for 22 percent of the bones,
    - cushions your joints,
    - makes up over 75 percent of our muscles,
    - regulates the body's temperature, and
    - removes all the waste from your body.

Water and Cancer

Based on a *New England Journal of Medicine* study, drinking 11 glasses of water per day may help keep bladder cancer away. They found that men who drink five glass of water daily have half the risk of those who drink one glass or less.

Water and Exercise

When should water be consumed with exercise? We should drink water before and after exercising. We should sip water every ten minutes of the work out. A couple of ounces every ten minutes or so is good. Water keeps your energy up and your weight down. It keeps your muscles strong and makes your joints supple. It also causes the digestive system to work smoothly and balances your whole system.

Cleansing and Detoxification

7-Day Cleansing Program

Pre Cleanse
One week prior to beginning cleanse—
- Eliminate tea, coffee, sugar, salt, biscuits, cakes, sweets, white bread, fried foods, and all flesh foods including all seafood.
- Avoid all alcohol consumption.
- If caffeine consumption is usually high, reduce gradually over a period of days.
- Do not be tempted to fill up with a huge meal of all your favorite foods on the night before your cleanse. It will postpone the cleansing and detoxification of your system.

Cleanse
The following foods must be eaten each day of your cleansing program:
- One cup of cooked brown rice,
- Unlimited vegetables (steamed or raw),
- One sweet potato per day or half of an avocado,
- Fruit (no citrus), and
- 12 raw almonds three to six times per day.

Whole Food Replacement Meals with plant-based protein mixes will alkalize and balance your body plus supplement your daily nutritional requirements of rich protein, fruits, and vegetables.

Use one dessert spoon of cold pressed oil (sunflower, safflower, or olive). Do not heat oil. Try mixed herbs, garlic, and lemon juice over salad.

* Garlic and herbs can be added to meals, but NO salt, pepper, or spices.*

(For all whole food recommend supplements, visit www.jamesdailministries.org)

Drinks

- On rising, drink three (3) to five (5) ounces of pure, filtered water with lemon juice.
- Minimum three (3) ounces of distilled water every 30 minutes if you weigh up to 150 pounds.
- Minimum four (4) ounces of distilled water every 30 minutes if you weigh 150-200 pounds.
- Minimum five (5) ounces of distilled water every 30 minutes if you weigh over 200 pounds.
- Herbal tea (no sugar or honey) (not to be substituted for water).

Helpful Advice

- Be prepared, shop for all groceries before starting the program.
- Do not keep tempting foods in your kitchen during your cleanse.
- No smoking or alcohol consumption during cleanse.
- Gentle exercise such as walking is recommended for 30 minutes each day.
- NO vigorous exercise, rest frequently.

While your body is cleansing, it is normal to experience symptoms such as headaches, nausea, skin eruptions, abdominal bloating, fatigue, and bad breath. These are all positive signs that your body is detoxifying and removing waste. These symptoms are temporary and will pass in a few days, leaving you with greater energy, mental clarity, and relief of previous symptoms.

PETEGAT Food
(Person Eating To Edify God's Amazing Temple)

Directions: **See PETEGAT Food instructions under *Foods and Recipes*.** For High Level Wellness, it is recommended that you use the PETEGAT Foods during and after the cleanse.

Breaking Your Cleanse

Breaking your cleanse gently and gradually is very important. Slowly introduce whole foods such as legumes (lentils, chickpeas, and soybeans) to your diet. Add vegetables and fruits, continuing with brown rice, and adding barley, oats, millet, and rye.

Common allergens such as wheat and corn should be introduced with care to check for any adverse reaction. Gradually keep introducing foods until a balanced whole food diet is achieved.

However, Daniel PURPOSED in his heart that he would not defile himself with the portion of the king's delicacies...Daniel said to the steward, "*Please test your servants for ten days, and let them give us pulse (vegetables, fruit, grains, lentils, beans...) to eat and water to drink. At the end of ten days their features appeared better and fatter in flesh than all the young men who ate the portion of the king's delicacies*" (Daniel 1:8, 12, 15 (paraphrased)).

High Level Wellness Plan

It is highly recommended that you complete the 7-Day Cleansing Program before beginning your High Level Lifestyle Changing Plan.

Fruit

three (3) or more servings per day (in season)

Legumes

two (2) or more servings per day (year-round)

Whole grains

five (5) or more servings per day (year-round)

Vegetables

four (4) or more servings per day (in season)

Eliminate ALL meats (including eggs) and dairy products (milk, cheese, and products from milk and cheese) from your diet. *(More information about milk can be found at www.gotpus.com and www.notmilk.com, or the Physicians Committee for Responsible Medicine's website at www.pcrm.org.)*

Eating For Vitality

One of the secrets of healthier and longer life is to eat food high in Vitamin and Mineral vitality. However, this is not the only criteria for judging foods. Good food should also be low in fat, salt, and fast-releasing sugars, high in fiber, and alkaline-forming. Non-animal sources of protein are desirable.

Such a lifestyle will also be low in calories. Eventually, you will not have to count calories because your body will become increasingly efficient and not crave extra food. A craving for food when you have already eaten enough calories is often a craving for more nutrients. Therefore, foods providing empty calories need to be avoided.

THE GOLDEN RULES FOR A HEALTHY DIET ARE:

Avoid
- sugar
- refined carbohydrates: white bread, rolls, cakes, refined foods
- coffee, tea, soft drinks with caffeine and cigarettes
- fried foods
- canned foods
- all potato chips

Eat more
- beans, lentils, and whole grains
- vegetables, raw or lightly cooked (in season)
- Eat at least three pieces of fresh fruit a day (in season)

Tips For High Level Wellness

Eat
- foods raw, if possible (in season);
- before dark—important for health and prevention of weight gain, and eat small, but nutrient-dense meals, like quinoa, brown rice, beans, legumes, or peas;
- flaxseed twice daily—grind only immediately before use, do not let it sit out, and put in cereal, oatmeal, shakes etc.;
- whole grain and organic cereal—when buying bread, the

first word in the ingredients should start with "whole" (recommend rye or pumpernickel);
- fifty percent raw fruits and vegetables—especially leafy green vegetables, eat plenty of cabbage, broccoli, brussel sprouts, cauliflower, and leeks (which contain sulfur and anti-carcinogenic properties);
- plenty of raw bananas, avocado, mangos and papaya—they are rich in enzymes; and
- one (1) cup of sprouts daily.

Avoid
- over-eating,
- eating under stress, and
- drinking while eating (drink 15 minutes before meals or 1.5 hours after).

Remember
- always eat breakfast (grains),
- chew foods well (minimum of 15 chews per bite),
- follow a fasting program once a month,
- use extra fiber daily—Flaxseed, beans, legumes, and whole grains are excellent sources of fiber, and move your bowels at least twice daily; and
- change to a natural toothpaste without fluoride and natural deodorant without aluminum.

Try Deep Breathing Exercises

This exercise helps to remove stress and depression, and increases oxygen in your body to prevent and help cure cancer. Get yourself into a comfortable position in a recliner chair or lie down on your bed. This can also be done while sitting up in a chair—just place both feet flat on the ground.

Place one hand over your belly—a few inches below the belly button. Your hand will give you feedback as to how you are doing on the breathing.

Close your eyes (not yet, though—read the rest of the directions first!). **Then slowly breathe in through your nose**. You do not have to take a particularly deep breath. What you are trying to do is take slow breaths. As you breathe in, you should feel your belly move out/ up against your hand. This is important because most people breathe incorrectly and were taught to suck in their stomachs and to stick their chests out. As you breathe in, your chest should stay relaxed and your belly should move out against your hand if you are sitting up, or up against your hand if you are lying down.

Once you have inhaled deeply and slowly, **hold your breath for a few seconds**. Do not wait until you feel anxious or panicky. **Then breathe out slowly through pursed lips even slower than you inhaled**. As you breathe out, feel your belly come back down and feel your shoulders and neck relax and sag.

Wait a few seconds and then do another breathing cycle. Practice for about 15 - 20 minutes once a day. If you have time to practice it more often, great; but it will still work with a once a day schedule. I usually suggest that people practice at night when they are already in bed and want to relax so that they can fall asleep. If you find yourself getting distracted during the exercise with thoughts about things you forgot to take care of or need to do, you can focus by reminding yourself to feel your belly against your hand. You can also help focus yourself by thinking "1" as you breathe in and "2" as you breathe out. It really does not matter what you use, as long as it is not too complicated.

*   *   *   *   *   *

LOSING WEIGHT THE HEALTHY WAY

Deprivation (not eating for a long time) leads to binging and long-term failure. The key to keeping your metabolism running smoothly is to eat every three hours during the day. Losing weight is not just a result of what you eat, but when you eat. If you wait more than three hours to eat, your body—

1) Passes its tipping point and launches a natural starvation protection mechanism. This starvation protection mechanism (spm) causes your body to preserve the most calorie-rich tissue to ensure your survival. This tissue is called FAT.

2) Begins to preserve body fat and cannibalize or eat away precious fat burning muscles.

3) Loses muscle tissue. Lean muscle tissue is what keeps your metabolism active, and, as a result, burns high levels of fat. For example, each pound of muscle burns approximately 50 calories per day with no activity. All it takes is to lose 5 pounds of muscle and your body burns 250 less calories per day. In the course of one year, this will result in 26 pounds of new fat.

4) Will have an increase in cortisol levels. Cortisol is a stress hormone that is closely associated with abdominal fat. Research has proven that eating every three (3) hours helps to reduce the levels of cortisol in your body. When these levels are reduced, your body will begin to burn BELLY FAT.

High Protein/Low Carbohydrate Diets

Any time you are on a high protein/low carbohydrate diet, you

---

will begin to lose 25 percent of lean muscle. The Atkins diet and many others like it have been a huge success in families all across America; yet research has proven that Dr. Atkins himself died at a weight normally considered obese and had a history of sugar (glycogen) stored in his muscles.

These diets can cause fatigue and depression, which lead to a sedentary (non-active) lifestyle, causing you to lose muscle faster. The key is to gain lean muscles, not lose them.

Healthy Weight Loss Plan

At Reformation Healing Ministries International, we do not focus on weight. We believe that the body will naturally balance itself if given the proper nourishment. However, we do have keys that will assist your body in building muscles and burning off fat. In your weight loss process, remember to have fun and relax. Losing weight the healthy way will give you a lifetime of results.

Keys
- Eat every three hours.
- DO NOT eat after dark.
- GET RID OF STRESS by eliminating the root causes.
- Drink recommended amounts water (refer to High Level Wellness).

Exercise

Exercise increases your metabolic rate as well as burns off calories. Be sure to get regular aerobic exercise, such as walking, running, bicycling, or swimming. Also, include stretching exercises for strength and flexibility. Exercise is better than an overly, strict diet for maintaining your health and controlling your weight. It is the best way to rid the body of fat and to maintain good muscle tone. Using light weights is the best way to rid the body of fat and to maintain good muscle tone.

Example of a Meal Plan
BREAKFAST (7:00 AM)
PETEGAT Food (quick meal)
SNACK (10:00 AM)
PETEGAT Food 2 ounces nuts (i.e.,13 walnuts) 1 ounce raisins (or dried fruit without sulfur dioxide)
LUNCH (1:00 PM)
Open-faced sandwich w/hummus, beans, tofu or Soy burger with whole grain bread; bean sprouts, spinach or avocado, tomatoes, Braggs Amino Acid, and cayenne pepper -OR- Salad*, Sandwich/ Hummus
SNACK (4:00 PM)
DINNER (7:00 PM)
Sweet potato with Earth Balance spread Vegan butter (from Health Food store), cinnamon, stevia, and pecans Salad Dressing: Braggs Amino Acid from the health food store, apple cider vinegar or lemon, Extra Virgin olive oil, and cayenne pepper. *You can modify according to personal taste; but avoid processed and cooked foods on salad, as well as processed salad dressings.*

Good Grains

Whole grains should be the foundation for optimal health. They provide the finest complex carbohydrates and fiber available in the entire food chain and the most energy to the human race than any other crop. You need more servings of grains than any other food. A few examples of good grains include barley, buckwheat, corn, millet, oats, quinoa, brown rice, rye, spelt, amaranth, and whole wheat.

Foods to Consume in Moderation

Apples, brown rice, buckwheat, chestnuts, corn, grapes, oatmeal, sweet potatoes, and yellow vegetables should all be consumed in moderation. These foods contain small amounts of essential fatty acid; but they should not be overused.

Snacks

If you must eat snacks occasionally to ward off hunger, make sure they are healthy. Good choices include:
- Celery and carrot sticks,
- Fresh applesauce and walnuts,
- Unsweetened gelatin made with fresh fruit in place of sugar and water,
- Natural, sugar-free whole grain muffins (made without dairy products; available in health food stores),
- Rice cakes topped with nut butter (but not peanut butter), and
- Watermelon, fresh fruit or frozen fresh fruit popsicles (available in health food stores).

Use wheat grass to calm the appetite. This is a very nutritious fuel from whole food that assists metabolic functions. Kelp seaweed is also beneficial.

*   *   *   *   *   *

DIET AND DIABETES

Please read this chapter very carefully because it may save you and your family a lot of pain, suffering, grief, or premature death. This is a proven recipe for success in preventing and curing diabetes. Diabetes is a diet disease; and it is curable. We have several testimonies to back that up. If we only follow what the scripture says in Genesis 1:29, which reads: *"And God said, 'Behold, I have given you every herb bearing seed, which is upon the face of all the earth and every tree in which is the fruit of a tree yielding seed, to you it shall be for food.'"*

So now, let us talk about the research based on the PCRM. First of all, "What is diabetes?" Diabetes occurs when the pancreas is not producing enough insulin—a hormone that ushers sugar into the cells of the body. Without insulin, the cell membrane keeps sugar out. This occurs when glucose—a simple sugar, which is the body's main fuel (energy), is present in the blood stream, but cannot get into the cells where it is needed.

There are two different types of diabetes—Type I, which is juvenile onset diabetes or childhood onset diabetes and Type II, which is more common and usually does not occur until adulthood. However, we are finding that more children are being diagnosed with Type II.

The problem with juvenile onset diabetes is an inadequate supply of insulin. Type I diabetes is in only about five to ten percent of all diabetic patients. It is usually transferred to babies during pregnancy based on the foods consumed by the mother. It is also found in people from the South (or those who are considered to be from the country).

Type II diabetes is primarily related to diet (eating habits) and medications. We have also found that some iatrogenic diseases—diseases acquired from health care facilities—have actually caused diabetes as well. Research has shown that people with Type II diabetes normally have plenty of insulin in the blood stream, but the cells are resistant to it. As a result, glucose cannot easily get into the cells and backs up in the blood stream. Over the short run, people with uncontrolled diabetes may experience fatigue, thirst, frequent urination, and blurred vision. In the end, they are at risk for heart disease, kidney failure, disorders of vision, blindness, nerve damage, and other difficulties.

Studies have also shown that people with Alzheimer's Disease have a basic foundation of diabetes. There are more than 40 million people in this country with diabetes; and the largest segment of that group is African Americans.

There are certain types of foods that researchers have contributed to diabetes. One of those is high fat. High dairy consumers and high fat consumers are setting themselves up for diabetes. In actuality, food can be a powerful tool in preventing and reversing diabetes. Diabetes can be reversed. Let me repeat that. "Diabetes can be reversed." We have testimonies to prove it.

I am a former diabetic. I found out that I had diabetes at the age of 26. When I changed my generational curse—(ignorance of food choices) diet/eating habits that were passed on for generations—I was cured. Many others who have changed their dietary habits to a plant-based whole food diet (PETEGAT), which we have incorporated at Reformation Healing Ministries International, have also reversed the curse of diabetes.

The focus of limited refined sugars and grains has always been the traditional approach to diabetes. Your doctor always tells you about limiting refined sugar and foods that release sugars during digestion, such as starches, breads, fruits, and pastas. Even if carbohydrates are reduced, the diet still may contain an unhealthy amount of fat and protein. Fats and protein are two of the main causes of diabetes. Diabetes experts in the past who were funded by the world systems (pharmaceutical industries) did not include fats and protein as a cause of diabetes. Today's experts (Physicians Committee for Responsible Medicine) are making it known that fats (especially saturated fats) and proteins contribute to the major incidence of diabetes in this country and around the world. The main source of saturated fats comes from animal products, such as meats, eggs, and dairy. Protein should be limited for people with impaired kidney function. Excess protein causes kidney failure.

The saturated fat that we consume is now getting more attention in the new approach to diabetes. The more fat there is in the diet, the harder it is for insulin to get glucose into the cells. Conversely, minimizing fat intake and reducing body fat helps insulin do a much better job. This can occur by getting on a new treatment program that drastically reduces meats, high fat, dairy products, and oils from the diet, while increasing grains, legumes, fruits, and vegetables. Remember Genesis 1:29 reads: "*And God said, behold I have given you every herb bearing seed, which is upon the face of all the earth, and every tree in which is the fruit of a tree yielding seed; to you it shall be for meat.*"

One study found that 21 of 23 patients on oral medication and 13 of 17 patients on insulin were able to get off their medication after 26 days on a near vegetarian diet and exercise program. During the two and three year follow-ups, most people with diabetes treated with this regime have retained their gains. Their dietary changes are simple, but profound; and they work. This means that low fat, vegetarian, or PETEGAT diets are ideal for people with diabetes.

In this book, I have included some of my own personal meal plans that will help eliminate and control diabetes. Other necessary treatments are also recommended to repair those organs for total healing and reversal of this disease.

In 2006, the PCRM, George Washington University, and the University of Toronto compared the health benefits of a low fat and refined vegan diet (excluding all animal products, including eggs, dairy, and meats and including unlimited vegetables, grains, fruits, and legumes) with a diet based on the American Diabetic Association (ADA) guidelines (which is used by the medical profession) in persons with Type II diabetes. Now remember, ADA guidelines do not limit fat or dairy in your diet. They will tell you to cut back on whole milk and use 2% milk. Yet, 2% milk contains up to 40 percent of fat. Tricky, huh? The results of this 22-week study were astounding.

They found that 43 percent of the vegan group reduced their diabetic medication compared to 26 percent of the ADA group. This was just a 22-week study. Among those whose medication remained constant, the vegan group lowered their hemoglobin A1C—an index of long term blood glucose—by 1.2 points, three times the change in the ADA group. Three times the difference in dealing with just the vegan diet. The vegan group lost an average of about 13 pounds compared to approximately 9 pounds for the ADA group. Among those participants who did not change their lipid lowering medication, the vegan group also had substantial decreases in their total and LDL cholesterol level compared to the ADA group.

Based upon what God told us in Genesis 1:29, the vegan diet (PETEGAT diet) is of what we need to partake. Now we know that one of the dietary approaches to preventing and reversing diabetes is to remove animal fat from our diet. Do not consume large quantities of oils. Avoid all vegetable oils. Use olive oil for cooking and other seed-based oils, such as avocado, flaxseed, almond, sunflower, and safflower for food preparation. Remember, these seed-based oils should not be used for cooking. Do not use Canola oil. It actually promotes diabetes. In fact, the dietary program mentioned in this book will explain the different types of diets that you need to do, including the raw food diet. The raw food diet of your diabetic program will speed the healing process (See Raw Food menus under *Foods and Recipes*).

If you focus on the new food group, which is based on whole plant foods; you can prevent or reverse most diseases. In as much, there are also some plant-based foods that should be avoided. For example, high glycemic index types of food such as, white or wheat bread, most cold cereals, white potatoes, refined sugars and grains. Watermelon and pineapple are also high glycemic in the fruit group.

Enjoy low glycemic index foods like pumpernickel bread or rye bread, multigrain bread, sourdough bread, old fashion oatmeal, grain cereal, grapenuts and most fruits. You can also enjoy sweet potatoes, whole grain pasta, brown rice, barley, quinoa, beans, peas, lentils, and most vegetables. Those foods can be consumed without limitations.

(You can obtain the supplement package that you need for the healing of diabetes by visiting our website at www.jamesdailministries.org or contacting the ministry.) We will give you the basic program for your diet and supplements to reverse diabetes within 90 days or less.

*   *   *   *   *   *

PLANT-BASED FOODS

Genesis 1:29 reads "*And God said, 'Behold, I have given you every herb bearing seed, which is upon the face of all the earth, and every tree, in which is the fruit of a tree yielding seed; to you it shall be for meat.*'"

God's Word is everlasting. It is perpetual; and it never changes. Therefore, if God said that we should be eating plant-based foods, then that should never change. In fact, I could not have gotten rid of my diseases until I reverted to what God said in His word in Genesis 1:29. I began to eat the fruits, vegetables, nuts, grains, and everything that grew out of the ground, and eliminated everything that walked on the ground. When I changed my eating habits (generational curse), then all the diseases went away—the diabetes, high blood pressure, the heart issues, and tuberculosis. I was even on seven different medications at one time. Reverting to the foods that God outlined in His Word changed my life. I stopped eating all the flesh-type foods and began to eat all plant-based foods; and now, I am in great health.

As we begin to move forward in this teaching, you will see all the benefits and the reasons why God advised us to eat plant-based foods. Remember that God designed the body; and He knows exactly what it needs to make sure that it receives the 120 years that he promised us in Genesis 6:3.

God said that we should eat plant-based foods. Since the devil was listening, he has us believing that "meat" means animal type foods. Meat means plant-based foods. When we see a meat market, we should look for plant-based food. But, what do we find? We find dead animals with all types of diseases in their bodies in the freezer cases of the grocery stores. The world is yet trying to advise us that we really need it for our health.

Board certified nutritionists and dieticians would tell you that meat (flesh) is something that we ought to have in order for us to get ample amounts of protein in our bodies. They tell us that we need to consume dairy to get enough calcium. That is untruthful. Over time, we have acquired a taste and now have an addiction to something that is causing diseases in our bodies. In this book, we discussed the dangers of meat and now we are going to focus on obtaining optimum health with the use of plant-based foods.

As you have read earlier, instead of using the terms vegetarian or vegan type food, I have developed a phrase, Person Eating to Edify God's Amazing Temple (PETEGAT). This is because many people get fearful when they hear the words vegetarian or vegan meals. You do not have to be a vegetarian to eat a vegetarian meal, as you do not have to be Spanish to eat Spanish meals, nor do you have to be Chinese to eat Chinese food. Eating fruits and vegetables is really part of the journey to total health and wellness.

Some vegans and vegetarians are sick because they eat everything from the plant even though it is not whole. If it is processed, then it is not healthy for you. For example, refined sugar is a byproduct of sugarcane, which is a plant. In all actuality, vegetarians can eat sugar and think it is healthy, or eat white rice and consider themselves eating properly. Vegetarianism first started because of people who were trying to protect the slaughtering of animals. They were animal rights protectors. I am trying to protect you from the diseases that penetrate God's sanctuary. It is good to protect our animals because we should not eat them.

As stated earlier, the word vegetarianism (PETEGAT) draws fear in the minds of people. God would never recommend something that is frightening or fearful. There are quite a few myths about vegetarian diets, including—

Myth #1 - *You will never get enough protein on a vegan or vegetarian diet.*

This is not true. Elementary biology teaches us that every cell in every plant has protein. How did that cow get its protein? Where did the elephant get its protein? Where do animals get their protein? The animals get their protein from grass. What about a gorilla? The gorilla's digestive system is almost identical to the human's. It processes and digests the fats and proteins almost the same as humans. Why do we think that we need to eat an animal to get protein when it is found in every cell of every plant?

Protein

Protein is an important nutrient required for the building, maintenance, and repair of tissues in the body. Protein is broken down into amino acids. The amino acids are building blocks for protein that can be synthesized (broken down) by the body or are ingested from food. The body makes protein as well. There are 20 different amino acids in protein and the body makes 11 of those 20. The other nine essential amino acids must be obtained from our diet. They can come from a variety of grains, legumes, beans, nuts, and vegetables.

It was once thought that a variety of plant foods did not have full protein, and were known as protein-combining or protein-complementing. This means that we have to eat something to complement the proteins that we obtain from plant-based foods. All of this research was influenced by the meat industry. Essential combining plants and meat is not necessary to get sufficient protein in the body. The required amount of protein needed for daily living may be obtained by eating a variety of vegetables, grains, beans, and legumes.

There are many vegetarians in other countries that are healthy and live without any mention of disease in their society. For example, a Cuban can only get approximately ½ pound of chicken, and ½ pound of beef a month. We eat that in one sitting. The Cubans have a club called the 120 Club in which people live to old age without diseases because they do not include meat as a main part of their diet. The Hunza tribe in Pakistan is a group of people who have never been exposed to the Western lifestyle; and these people live to be more than 100 years old. They have no trace of heart attacks, strokes, or any health issues. They normally die of natural causes. This goes back to God's 120 years promise to us (Genesis 6:3) based on eating his plants as stated in Genesis 1:29.

How much protein does the body need? The recommended daily allowance (RDA) for the average sedentary adult is 0.8 gram/kilogram of the body weight. To find out your RDA, multiply your body weight times (x) 0.36 gram/kilogram. For example, if you weigh 130 pounds, you only need 47 grams of protein per day. Most people get more than 47 grams of protein in one meal.

Major sources of protein for those who eat PETEGAT meals include:

4 ounces of tempeh = 20 grams of protein
1 typical Veggie burger = 15 grams of protein
8 ounces Soy Milk = 10 grams of protein
1 cup black bean soup = 16 grams of protein
1 Peanut butter sandwich = 20 grams of protein
1 cup pasta with vegetables = 18 grams of protein

Based upon their research, the PCRMis still making recommendations. For example, Japanese people have a higher life expectancy rate than Americans because of their incorporated soy-based diet.

Researchers in health and nutrition science have determined that the average female only needs 34 grams of protein per day, and the average male needs a maximum of 45 grams. Now consider that this is recommended even for males over 180 pounds. I weigh 210 pounds, and I get about 25-30 grams of protein per day. A horse or even gorilla that eats grass gets much less protein a day than we do; and they are stronger and more muscular. Protein is overrated in this country.

Myth #2 - *You can get anemia if you do not eat red meat.*
That is also not truthful. If you look at a biology book or study anything to do with botany, you will know that anemia is a result of low concentration of iron in our blood. A higher quality of iron is found in beans, grains, and vegetable sources than is found in meat. There is absolutely no evidence that vegetarians are at a higher risk for anemia than meat eaters.

Myth #3 - *You can never get enough calcium if you do not drink milk.*
Milk is a detriment to our bodies. There are many plant-based foods that have higher concentrations of calcium than milk. Certain fruits and vegetables have more calcium than milk. Green leafy vegetables, especially collard greens, have as much as seven times more

calcium than milk. The world has really influenced us to do things that are contrary to health and cause diseases. We often times have to find remedies to correct diseases that we have acquired because we did not follow what God instructed us to do in Genesis 1:29.

There are high levels of calcium in various nuts (almonds) than in dairy products. Dairy is a major cause of diseases.

Examples of food with high calcium content include:

10 dried figs = 269mg
Vegetarian baked beans = 128mg
2 ½ cups of Navy Bean soup = 200mg
1 baked sweet potato = 70mg
1 tofu hot dog = 20mg
1 bowl whole grain cereal and ½ cup soy milk = 150mg

Myth #4 - *Vegetarians lack Vitamin B$_{12}$ in their diets.*

Vegetarians do get sufficient B$_{12}$ in their diets. As a matter of fact, hundreds of years ago, people who ate plant-based diets were able to get vitamin B$_{12}$ from the soil. Vitamin B$_{12}$ comes from sources that are contaminated with bacteria. Individuals need to make sure they get adequate B$_{12}$ in their diets. Seaweed and sea vegetation like kelp and wakames are excellent food sources for vitamin B$_{12}$. Other options include fortified juices, cereals, and soymilk.

We need to make sure that we take whole food supplements no matter what we are eating because we are not getting enough nutrients from the foods we eat today. The soil has been over-harvested and over-planted. The soil does not sit long enough to reproduce the various chemicals that plants need to absorb. The Department of Agriculture states that we would have to eat 78 bowls of spinach today in order to get the same amount of nutrients in a bowl as we did in 1948. *(Visit our website to get recommendations on whole food supplements that are good for the body).*

Vegetables and Aging

Parents always tell their children to eat their vegetables. Research on vegetables and aging has found that vegetables help to keep the brain young and slow the mental decline oftentimes associated with growing old. A six-year study done in 2000 concluded that mental sharpness of older adults who ate more than two servings of grains and vegetables daily appeared five years younger than those who ate fewer or no vegetables. This research was headed by Martha Clare Morris of Rush Institute for Healthy Aging at Chicago's Rush University Medical Center. The study consisted of both men and women. Researchers found that green leafy vegetables, including collard greens, spinach, and kale, appeared to be the most beneficial. They believe this is so because they contain a healthy amount of the antioxidant Vitamin. The research determined getting Vitamin E straight from the plant helps keep the brain young.

A study published in the *Journal of Neurology* and funded with grants from the National Institute on Aging has shown that the fats from healthy oils can keep cholesterol low and arteries clear, which contribute to brain health.

Dr. Meir Stampfer of Harvard School of Public Health said that the Chicago study is a good study and holds true to the benefit of vegetables to the body. In fact, research has also determined that those who ate more than two servings of vegetables per day had less than 40 percent mental decline compared to those who ate fewer vegetables. Harvard University School of Public Health conducts many research studies on the impact of vegetables on the brain. In His Word, Genesis 1:29, God tells us what we need to eat—fruits and vegetables—to stay young.

Soy Products

A study from the American Journal of Epidemiology finds that soy foods may lower the risk of ovarian cancer. The California Teachers Study cohort researched 97,275 women, and determined that soy stops the incidence of ovarian cancer by 44 percent. Tofu and soymilk are excellent sources of soy.

Plant-Based Foods and Dementia

The British Medical Association of Neurology and Psychiatry published a research study done in South Korea, which tracked the dementia development of 518 elder adults for two to four years. They found that a vitamin, folic acid, which is found in leafy vegetables, fruits, and beans, helped create improvement in short term memory, mental agility, and verbal fluency among adults over age 50 who took over 1800mcg. The US recommends 400mcg of folic acid per day, which is found in two servings of collard greens, dried beans, avocadoes, kale, spinach, or lettuce. Folic Acid is the same as Vitamin B9. According to the study, a lack of folate may triple the risk of developing dementia.

Preventing Diabetes

Diabetes is a major disease that is affected by what we eat. A PETEGAT diet consisting of all plant-based food is the best way to control and prevent diabetes. As we mentioned earlier, in treating Type II diabetes, all dairy and animal-type protein need to be eliminated from your diet. Your physician or nutritionist may not tell you to stop eating meat or dairy. *(More information on the research studies done by the PCRM on diabetes can be obtained from their website at <u>www.pcrm.org</u>).*

It is recommended that you restrict your portion sizes. Too much of a good thing is not healthy. Do not have more than three things at a sitting. A lot of evidence suggests that a different dietary approach would be easier to follow if you stick to plant-based foods. Do not eat any processed-type plants. They are just as bad as eating dairy and meat.

Saturated Fats

In this book, we advocate the PETEGAT lifestyle. Are you eating to edify God? Would God be happy? A plant-based diet is very low in saturated fats. As mentioned earlier, saturated fat is responsible for cancer and other diseases, and has a lot to do with diabetes. Saturated fat blocks the uptake of insulin into the cells.

Saturated fats can also be found in coconut, palm, and kernel oil. Saturated fats are directly related to higher levels of cholesterol. It is greatly advised to avoid using vegetable oils and re-heated/recycled oils; because they break down into free radicals. These free radical lose electrons due to the chemical reactions caused by the heating process.

When the oils molecules lose electrons they become oxidized. The ingested oxidized molecules (free radicals) have an adverse reaction to our cellular structure. These free radicals want to be balanced so they attack our healthy cells in our body. The free radicals strip away the electrons from our healthy cells leaving them incomplete. A free radical will attempt this attack for up to 10,000 times a day. Similarly, avoid eating any hydrogenated oils especially margarine. Margarine is one molecule away from being plastic. Margarine is a deadly man made product that we have added to our diet.

Glycemic Index and Blood Sugar
Glycemic index identifies foods that increase blood sugar rapidly and allow you to favor foods that have a negative effect on blood sugar. High glycemic foods include sugar, white potatoes, most wheat flour products, wheat bread, watermelon, pineapple, and cold cereals. You do not want high-glycemic index foods in your diet. Low-glycemic index foods can be enjoyed and eaten until you are satisfied. Rye bread, oats, grape nuts, most fruits, sweet potatoes, pasta, brown rice, beans, peas, lentils, and most vegetables are low-glycemic index foods. There is a reason why God told us to eat plant-based foods. It is healthier; and you live longer in perfect and good health.

*   *   *   *   *   *

GOOD FOODS/BAD FOODS

DISEASE-CAUSING FOODS	TOTAL WELLNESS FOODS
Acid-forming foods: all meat and fish, milk products, tea, coffee, chocolate, sugar, and fat	**Alkaline-forming foods:** all fresh fruit and vegetables, millet, almonds, Brazil nuts, herbal teas, and bean sprouts
High-fat foods: meat, dairy products, including butter, cheese, ice cream, margarine, and vegetable oils	**Low-fat foods:** soy milk, tofu, beans, vegetables, and fruits
Meat protein foods: all meat, (i.e., beef, pork, lamb, turkey, duck, goat, chicken and fish)	**Non-meat protein foods:** beans, brown rice, lentils, nuts, seeds, and tofu
Fast-releasing sugars: white, brown, and raw sugar; molasses, maple syrup, glucose, malt, honey, and most forms of syrups. *(If you use any sugar at all other than stevia, use molasses, maple syrup, and raw sugar (very moderately)).*	**Slow-releasing sugars:** fresh fruit and unprocessed whole grains (i.e., muesli, brown rice, lentils, and beans)
High-sodium foods: salt, including sea salt, yeast extracts, all smoked fish, most cheeses, crisps, salted nuts, most canned foods, and soy sauce	**High-potassium foods:** fruit, including pineapple, grapes, and bananas, vegetables, dandelion tea, and chicory tea
Refined foods: white flour, white, brown and raw sugar, white rice, processed and most packaged foods.	**Unrefined foods:** nuts, seeds, whole grains, whole meal flour and bread, lentils, beans, and brown rice

CANCER CELLS

Many things in our everyday life, including what we eat, drink, and breathe, are major causes of cancer. Johns Hopkins University recently concluded extensive research on cancer and released an update. Their research has concluded that:

1) Every individual has cancer cells in his or her body. All cancers begin in cell—the body's basic unit of life. The cells do not show up in a standard test until they have multiplied to a few billion and have created a mass. When doctors tell cancer patients that there are no more cancer cells in the body after treatment, it just means the test is unable to detect the cancer cells because they have not reached the detectable size.

   There is a reason that God placed cancer cells in every human body. God wants to ensure that we are obedient to His Word. As we go down the list of things that causes cancer, you will see that God did not sanction any of them. It is a choice that we make based on the influence of the world system, which, in fact, is influenced by Satan.

   The world is saying, "Let us find a cure for cancer." How could it be? It is like saying there is a cure for red blood cells. Cancer cells are part of the body. There is no cure for cancer cells. We need to prevent the cells from uncontrolled growth by building a strong immune system. Cancer is an immune disease. If our immune system is weak, then we are at greater risk of getting cancer and other diseases. However, cancer tumors can be healed and prevented.

2) Cancer cells occur between six to more than ten times in a person's lifetime.

3)   When a person's immune system is strong, the cancer cells will be destroyed and prevented from multiplying and forming tumors.

4)   When a person has cancer, it indicates this person has multiple nutritional deficiencies. These can be due to genetic, environmental, food, and lifestyle factors.

Remember that "genetic" is "ignorance." It is a generational curse, which is ignorance. We were told that everything that tastes good is good for us; and we carry the same lifestyle forward.

5)   To overcome the multiple nutritional deficiencies, changing our diets and including supplements will strengthen the immune system. In this book, there are several different areas that contain menus and information on how to prevent the different types of cancers. If you follow the information in this book, cancer will not be a problem in your life.

6)   Chemotherapy involves poisoning the rapidly-growing cancer cells and destroying the rapidly-growing healthy cells in the bone marrow, gastrointestinal tract, etc. It also causes organ damage, like liver, kidneys, heart, lungs, and other illnesses. It destroys everything.

7)   While destroying cancer cells, radiation also burns, scars, and damages healthy cells, tissue, and organs. God did not plan for us to be under a system that would destroy us. God is in the healing business. It is critically important that the church teach its members how to create strong immune systems. We can win the battle if we make the right choices.

8)   The initial treatment with chemotherapy and radiation will often reduce the size of the tumor. However, prolonged use of chemotherapy and radiation do not result in more tumor destruction. Doctors will put a patient on radiation and chemotherapy for an extended period of time, knowing that

the results usually occur within the first three treatments. More treatment means more money for the doctors.

9) When the body has too much toxic burden from chemotherapy and radiation, the immune system is either compromised or destroyed. Hence, the person succumbs to various kinds of infections and complications. Why would you take something that would destroy the system that God designed in the body to protect the body from diseases?

10) Chemotherapy and radiation can cause cancer cells to mutate and become resistant and difficult to destroy. Surgery can also cause cancer cells to spread to other areas.

Many patients with cancer come to my office for counseling and often want immediate results. They leave their medical doctor's office believing that have incurable cancer. Oncologists have burned them with radiation, destroying their cells and immune system. Nothing can be healed with a weak immune system. I have to regain hope in these individuals, and then place them on a protocol that will rebuild their immune system and decrease the growth of the cancer cells.

11) An effective way to battle cancer is to starve the cancer cells by not feeding them with the foods they need to multiply.

The Noble Prize in medicine in the 1950s was a cure for cancer. It was presented to Dr. Otto Warburg who discovered that cancer cells live off sugar; and oxygen will destroy them. How many of you have heard an oncologist say that if you stop using sugar then you can fight cancer? That is not true. We need to promote prevention; and the only way for that to occur is to have a strong immune system.

Cancer Feeds on:
Sugar and Table Salt
Sugar is a cancer-feeder. Cutting out sugar cuts off one important

food supply to the cancer cells. Do not use NutraSweet, Equal, Spoonful, and other sugar substitutes. They are made with the poison aspartame that causes cancer. A better natural sweetener would be a little molasses or Stevia. Avoid all table salt. Healthy alternatives for table salt include Braggs Amino Acid or sea salt.

Milk

Milk causes the body to produce mucus, especially in the gastrointestinal tract. Cancer feeds on mucus. Cutting out milk and all dairy products and substituting unsweetened soy starves the cancer cells.

Acidic Environment

Cancer cells thrive in an acidic environment. A meat-based diet is high in acid. Some acidic meats include fish, chicken, pork, beef, lamb, goat, turkey, etc. Meat also contains livestock antibiotics, growth hormones, and parasites, which are all harmful, especially to people with cancer. The immune system needs to be as strong as possible.

Other Foods

A diet made of fruits, vegetables, nuts, and grains is healthy. You can drink vegetable juices of four to six ounces per serving. Avoid coffee, tea, chocolate, and other foods high in caffeine. Green tea is a better alternative and has cancer-fighting properties.

Water is important. Hydrogenated water is a better option. *(Additional information about hydrogen sticks for your water can be found on our website)*. Distilled water is acidic and should be avoided. Another good option is purified or filtered water.

Meat

Meat protein is difficult to digest and requires many digestive enzymes. Undigested meat remaining in the intestines becomes putrefied and leads to more toxic buildup, which provides more toxic energy to cancer.

Cancer cell walls have a tough protein covering. Refraining from eating meat frees more enzymes to attack the protein walls of the cancer cells. This allows the body's killer cells to destroy the cancer cells.

Supplements such as Vitamin E help build the immune system. *Visit our website to see the types of supplements that you will need to enhance and build the immune system.*

Emotions and Cancer

Cancer is a disease of the mind, body, and spirit. A proactive and positive spirit will help the cancer warrior be a survivor. Anger, unforgiveness, and bitterness put the body into a stressful and acidic environment. Learn to have a loving and forgiving spirit. Learn to relax and enjoy life.

Our emotions control the development of tumors in the body. Elements of emotions can actually shut down the body. For example, a person who harbors anger will cause the liver to function less than normal. The liver performs about 600 functions every minute. If you are angry, then the body will not be able to respond to certain chemicals, because the liver is not able to perform the functions for which God has designed it.

Cancer cells cannot thrive in an oxygenated environment. Daily physical exercises and deep breathing exercises (see the *Deep Breathing* section in this book for instructions) may actually promote the destruction of cancer cells in the body.

Other Cancer Preventing Tips

There are many things that can be done to increase oxygen in the cells.

1) Use hydrogenated water to rebuild hydrogen.
2) Be mindful of using plastic containers and using microwaves. The energy from the microwave creates dioxins, which are harmful and poisonous to the cells in the body.
3) Do not use plastic wraps in the microwave. (This reflects a recent study conducted by Johns Hopkins University). Dr. Edward Fujimoto, who heads the Wellness program at Castle Hospital, has also released a lot of information about microwave cooking.

Our foods should not be in plastic wrap.
4)   Use porcelain and wax papers to protect your foods.

Remember, it is important to be proactive. Do not allow cancer to take over your life or the lives of your loved ones. Gather all the information that you need from this book and use it not only for yourself, but communicate it to others. We can win this cancer battle based on prevention. It is important to keep a strong immune system. Loving one another and giving are ways to keep a healthy immune system. Eat your fruits, vegetables, nuts, and grains. Playing classical music is one way to relax the body and boost the immune system. Always keep a positive attitude.

*   *   *   *   *   *

ALL MEATS CAUSE CANCER AND OTHER DISEASES

We have learned over the years that meat is a major cause of cancer. Processed meat raised the bar quite a bit because of the chemicals added to it to make it look good (bright pink or red). Even things that are added, including sodium chloride, are used to ensure that it is fresh-looking. It is oftentimes distorted based on the health concerns that are associated with meat, including processed meats. This writing is based on major studies done all over the world. You should beware of processed meats, such as, hot dogs, hamburgers, luncheon meat, sliced ham, turkey, etc.

Major studies and research on processed meats were conducted by the American Institute for Cancer Research and the World Cancer Research Fund. Their researches show that no amount of processed meat is completely safe. This international panel of experts spent five years developing this particular report after reviewing more than 7,000 large-scale studies. *(For more information, or to view the reports, visit www.dietandcancerreport.org)*.

Reports have shown that excess body fat increases the risk of cancer of the colon, kidney, pancreas, esophagus, uterus, and postmenopausal breasts. Many people do not consider themselves as high-risk for cancer because of their weight. Weight is not the primary factor. It is the lifestyle! I have seen many individuals who come to my clinic and are at the normal weight for their gender, height, and age; but they are usually sicker than the ones who are overweight. We put a lot of emphasis on weight because reports are generally based on the problems associated with being overweight. Researchers determined that one of the major factors for being overweight is consuming sausage, bacon, luncheon meat, hot dogs, canned meat, and deli meat. Overweight people are not the only ones who eat processed meat.

Processed meat not only causes cardiovascular disease, high blood pressure, and arthritis. We now have to consider that it not only affects people who are overweight or obese. Karen Collins, a Cancer Institute nutrition advisor, stated, "People forget that body fat is not an inner glob that we carry around on their waist and thighs. It is a metabolically active tissue that produces substance in the body that promotes the development of cancer. People that eat the same thing, whether they are overweight or not, are going to experience the same effects of cancer."

Michael Thun, head of the Epidemiological Research for American Cancer Society, says, "People are not paying nearly enough attention between the relationship of obesity and increased cancer risk." The report also found that every 1.7 ounces of processed meat consumed a day increases the risk of colorectal cancer by 21 percent. Could you imagine eating ½ pound or even a pound of processed meat? That would almost guarantee that you will develop cancer. Researchers state that this should be a wake-up call for those who eat hotdogs or pepperoni pizza regularly. Those individuals should look for another alternative.

The Cancer Research team believes that there are several reasons why processed and red meats may increase the risk of cancer. One of those reasons is carcinogen, which is linked to smoked meats and excess salt and nitrate in the meats.

The evidence linking red meat intake (beef, pork, and lamb) to colorectal cancer is more convincing than it was a decade ago. In 2005, after more than 23 years and 148,000 volunteers, the American Medical Association concluded that red meat is a major cause of colorectal cancer. The PCRM also said that their research on food intake and animal by-product determined that white meat is three times more carcinogenic than red meat. We have been lied to about which meat is more dangerous. All meats are dangerous.

Limiting the red meat to 18 ounces of cooked meat per week can minimize the risk of cancer. If meat causes cancer at a certain level, how can you be sure that the small amount is not going to cause cancer? If they are saying that 18 ounces of cooked meat will cause MINIMUM risk of cancer; then who wants minimum cases of cancer when you can eliminate all cases? Eating 18 ounces of meat per week works out to three ounces per day.

If you read the article, you will know that James 4:17 reads, "*Therefore to him that knoweth to do good, and doeth it not, to him it is sin.*" If you eat the meats that are cancer-causing agents, then you know that it is against God's Will, which is sin. You cannot sin within the body and not sin against the Spirit.

Five Worst Foods to Grill

In The Cancer Project study conducted in August 2005 by the PCRM, they found that according to the Hearth Patio and Barbeque Association, many people are unaware of the cancer-producing compounds in certain foods that they grill.

The main compound, heterocyclic amines (HCA), is part of the family of mutagenic cancer-causing compounds. Studies show that HCA contains the highest concentration. Nutrition professionals with the cancer project determined that different foods have higher concentrations. HCA is produced through the cooking of many animal products including chicken, beef, pork, lamb, goat, and fish.

The federal government officially added HCA to its list of known carcinogens. They have found that many commonly-grilled foods have high levels of HCA. The top five worst foods to grill are chicken, steak, pork, salmon, and hamburger.

GRILLED FOOD	HCA LEVEL
Chicken breast (skinless, boneless,	14,300ng/3.5 ounces
Steak (grilled or well done)	810ng/3.5 ounces
Barbecued pork	407ng/3.5 ounces
Salmon (grilled with skin)	166ng/3.5 ounces
Hamburger (grilled or well done)	130ng/3.5 ounces

Chicken

Boneless, skinless, grilled, and well-done chicken breast is the worst food to grill. They measured this by finding out the HCA level. HCAs are measured as ng/100g; and the nutrition professionals found that chicken breast has 14,300ng for every 3.5 ounces.

As you can see, grilling these meats creates a higher cancer risk. We often believe that we are doing something healthy, family oriented, and festive; but the devil uses that as an opportunity to move in and destroy the sanctuary of God. The devil influences man to select a food other than what God told us what to eat in Genesis 1:29.

Researchers have found that choosing plant-based foods instead of meats lowers cancer risk. Fruits and vegetables are not only low in fat and high in fiber. They also contain many cancer-fighting substances like carotenoids. Carotenoids—the pigment that gives fruits and vegetables their dark colors—have been shown to help prevent cancer. Cooked meats cause cancer; and vegetables and fruits prevent cancer. Beta-carotene, present in many dark green and yellow vegetables, helps protect against lung cancer and helps prevent cancers of the bladder, mouth, larynx, esophagus, breast, and other sites. Many studies have found that diets rich in fruits and vegetables— in season and low in animal fat—decrease the risks of cancer.

We need to eat our fruits and vegetables in season. God has allowed His plants to bear food in certain times of the year based upon our needs. One thing that God has directed us to do in His word is to store grain. "Grain" means meal. Our meals should be prepared around grains. Grain is any seed that gives life including beans, legumes, brown rice, quinoa, and oats. These foods all fight cancer. We can now understand why Daniel refused to eat from the King's table. He ate just pulse grain for ten days. He wanted to show that eating grain would make you look better, smarter, and have better health. Remember that the King's table consisted of high fat and a lot of meat. The Babylonian food was sinful and caused diseases in the body.

The Other Dangers of Cooked Food

Grilling meat also produces other types of food mutagens. Grilling or broiling meat over a direct flame results in fat dropping on the fire and the production of polycyclic aromatic hydrocarbon-containing flames. Polycyclic aromatic hydrocarbons (PAHs) adhere to the surface of food. The more intense the heat, the more PAHs are present. They are widely believed to play a significant role in causing cancer.

Researchers have found an association between grilled or broiled, not fried, meat consumption and stomach cancer. It implies that dietary exposure to PAHs may play a role in the development of stomach cancer. All meats cause cancer; and your risk can be increased based on how it is prepared.

Hotdogs, Red Meat, Chicken, and Fish

Another meat that is often grilled is hotdogs. The study shows that HCAs do not form in grilled hotdogs. These highly-processed meat products contain other carcinogens like nitrates and nitrite compounds and preservatives. Grilled hotdogs and sausages have been recognized as potent carcinogens. The increased dietary intake of processed meat has been linked to all types of cancers including colon and pancreatic cancers. Pancreatic cancer is one of the most prevalent kinds of cancer caused by processed meat because people make sandwiches and eat on the run.

Recent studies show that red meat can increase colon cancer risk as much as 300 percent based on the lack of fiber and too much fat in the meat.

Many believe that chicken and fish are healthy. Research shows that chicken and fish are a known cause of carcinogens. On the grill, chicken produced more than ten times the amount of carcinogenic HCA found in grilled beef.

Foods You May Grill

Portobello mushrooms, veggie burgers, and vegetables are good options to grill and prevent harmful carcinogens. There are 21 different areas of research that are associated with grilled meat and cancer risk. There is a reason in Genesis 1:29 why God gave us a specific warning as to what we need to eat, which reads, *"And God said, 'Behold, I have given you every herb bearing seed, which is on the face of all the earth, and every tree, in which is the fruit of a tree yielding seed; to you it shall be for meat.'"* God knew exactly what we needed and that meat would be a major cause of cancer.

* * * * * *

HEALTHY EXCHANGES

AVOID	REPLACEMENT
Eggs	Crumbled tofu (scrambled), 1 tablespoon milled flaxseed mixed w/3 tablespoon water
Fried Foods	Baked, boiled, steamed or broiled foods
Canned Foods	Fresh or fresh frozen foods (limit frozen)
Caffeine	Yerba mate (health food store)
All forms of refined sugar (white sugar, brown sugar)	Stevia, maple syrup (not pancake), powdered barley, malt sweetener, and corn sweetener
Salt	Braggs Amino Acid (health food store)
White flour products	Whole grains
White rice	Brown rice
Alcohol (including beer and wine)	Herbal teas
Soft drinks	Sparkling water mixed w/ unsweetened fruit juice
Animal fat, found in butter, cream, mayonnaise, rich dressings	Avocados, olives, raw nuts, raw seeds, olive oil, and soy mayonnaise
Yeast foods (mushrooms, peanuts)	Wheat germ, corn germ (use fresh Shitake mushroom in moderation)
Vegetable/Canola oils (for cooking)	Olive oil

DRUG FACTS

In Revelation 18:23c-24, the word "sorcery" means pharmaceutical drugs. We believe God designed foods and herbs to assist the body in healing itself. Man-made synthetic drugs (prescriptions/pharmaceutical drugs) will only cause the body to become more diseased. Extensive research has proven that these drugs are extremely harmful, and many times deadly.

In the *Charlotte Observer* dated July 21, 2006, the Institute of Medicine (Institute) provided an alarming report about medication errors. The report stated that at least 1.5 million Americans are sickened, injured, or killed each year by avoidable errors in prescribing, dispensing, and taking medications. Medical errors are so prevalent in hospitals that, on average, a patient is subject to a medication error each day he or she fills a hospital bed.

Following up on its 2000 report on medical errors of all kinds, the Institute, a branch of the National Academies, undertook the most extensive study ever of medication errors at the request of Congress when it passed the Medicare Modernization Act in 2003. The report found errors to be costly. The study reported that the extra medical costs of drug-related injuries occurring only in hospitals estimated to be $3.5 billion a year.

The errors the Institute studied included doctors writing illegal prescriptions, nurses giving one patient medication intended for another, and a local pharmacist dispensing 100mg pills rather than the prescribed 50mg. The report also stated that based on existing studies, the panel estimated that drug errors cause at least 400,000 preventable injuries and deaths in hospitals each year, more than 800,000 in nursing home facilities for the elderly, and 530,000 among Medicare recipients treated in outpatient clinics. The report said the actual numbers are likely to be much higher. The above article was stated in the *Charlotte Observer*. According to the Food and Drug Administration, the Center for Disease Control, and the Public Citizen Research Group, one year of adverse prescription reactions included:

- 61,000 people with induced Parkinsonism;
- 32,000 hip fractures, including 1,500 deaths;
- 16, 000 injurious car crashes;
- 163,000 with memory loss;
- 659,000 hospitalizations;
- 28, 000 cases of life-threatening or fatal reactions to dioxin (digitalis);
- 41,000 hospitalizations;
- 3,300 deaths from aspirin-like compounds; and
- 9.6 million older adults per year are hospitalized due to adverse drug reactions.

* * * * * *

THE TRUTH BEHIND VACCINATIONS

Following are some vaccine quotes that are worth repeating.

1) *"The only safe vaccine is one that is never used"* by Dr. James R. Shannon, former director of the National Institutes of Health.

2) *"Live virus vaccines against influenza or poliomyelitis may in each instance produce the disease it intended to prevent. The live virus against measles and mumps may produce such side effects as encephalitis (brain damage)"* by Jonas and Darrell Salk, 1977.

3) *"The death rate from smallpox was actually higher among those who had been vaccinated."*

4) *"It took over three years of research before we looked at each other and said, 'vaccines are killing babies.'"*

5) *"It is a well documented fact that the incidence and mortality from infectious disease fell from 90 percent well before any vaccine was even introduced. So the United States mandated vaccination and it resulted in a three fold increase in whooping cough."*

6) *"This is not a rare occurrence. Epidemics in fully vaccinated populations are a rule rather than an exception."*

Experts from all over the world are beginning to realize that vaccines are precursors to other major diseases. Thirty years ago, Chief Executive Henry Gadsden of Merck—one of the largest pharmaceuticals in the world—told *Fortune Magazine* of his distress that the company's potential markets had been limited only to sick people. He suggested that he wanted Merck to be more like chewing-gum maker, Wrigley's. Gadsden said that it had long been his dream to make drugs for healthy people so that Merck will be able to sell to everyone. Three decades later, the Alliances for Human Research Protection stated that the late Henry Gadsden's dream has come true.

Many states are mandating vaccines for papilloma virus to girls as young as eleven years old. Based on research, all companies and some medical doctors are promoting aspirin as a preventive medicine for heart attacks and strokes. Unfortunately, the aspirin causes gastroenteritis and cancer. The drug companies are very successful in selling drugs to healthy people.

In 2005, the Centers for Disease Control (CDC) said that they went back 40 years and have not found one person who has claimed that the flu vaccine has saved their life. The flu vaccine contributes to Alzheimer's Disease, dementia, and a host of other diseases. They have conquered that dream of inventing drugs for healthy people. There are just a few vaccines with no side effects that are currently being taken by healthy people to ward off diseases.

One thing that we need to be conscious of is not to let the world (government) force any type of vaccination on our children before obtaining adequate information from independent researchers. The federal government will support the pharmaceuticals because the pharmaceutical companies provide campaign money to many politicians. We have to revert to the church to lead us through this devastating crisis.

We have been told repeatedly that certain things are incurable. What did God say about incurable diseases? He said that there is no such thing as incurable diseases. Let us follow the Word of God because He said that if we obey Him, then He will remove all of your diseases (Psalms 103:3).

*   *   *   *   *   *

MEDICAL FREEDOM

There are laws that are enacted by a certain group of medical (Allopathic) practitioners. There are laws in certain states that make it illegal to say that a person can be healed. As you know, David talked about the benefits of the Lord in Psalms 103:3, which reads, "*Who forgiveth all thine iniquities; who healeth all thy diseases*." If the Word of God says that God will heal all of our diseases, and the world says that they are incurable diseases; who do we believe? Do we believe the Word of God or the world?

God told Jeremiah (Jeremiah 46:11) that all the medicines in the world are not going to heal the people, but to go to Gilead and get the balm that will heal his people. The Balm of Gilead is sap from a tree. If God had to send His people to get some natural herbs; then why not the church?

Reflecting back on my childhood, very rare in my household did we go to the doctor. Whatever illness we had, my mother had a remedy from different teas and barks from trees for that particular sickness. For example, we would make herbal tea from the forest to treat the flu, and within a day, we would be back in school. The laws of this country would say that what my mother did was wrong. Many do not enact those laws unless people receive a tremendous amount of healing.

There were signers of the Declaration of Independence who knew a day would come when one group of doctors would try to shut down another group. Dr. Benjamin Rush, a signer of the Declaration of Independence, stated, "Unless we put medical freedom into the Constitution, the time will come when medicine will organize into an undercover dictatorship to restrict the art of healing to one class of men and deny equal privileges to others. The Constitution of this Republic should make a special privilege for medical freedom as well as religious freedom."

* * * * * *

PRAY FOR OUR HEALTH CARE PROFESSIONALS

Churches need to come together in intercessory prayer for our children, nieces, nephews, mothers, fathers, and the Saints of God throughout the land. Many individuals are under the control of a system—pharmaceutical or the world health care system—that God did not sanction. We do not want you to be misconstrued that doctors are terrible people. My youngest daughter is a pediatrician. She does her best based on what she was taught; although she had been taught by a system that actually causes a lot of harm to the people who have been treated.

All drugs have side effects; and God does not want you to stay under that. There are times when a drug may keep you alive until you begin to change some things in your life. In our Statement of Faith, you will see that we believe in invasive types of health care. We do not believe that drugs and surgery are the only recourse for a person with diseases. The churches believe that diseases are incurable because the world says so. Based upon testimonies I have received from people all over the world, my healing ministry has proven to cure many. I encourage them to change their lifestyle, and to do what Daniel did by refusing the Babylonian food.

There are nurses, medical doctors, and technicians who are working on the front line and have been touched in a negative way by the world's health care system. I teach doctors that they need another way to deal with the health of God's people. They started out to help; but they find out that the system is not designed to help. It is not the individual doctor, but rather the system that is under the guidance of the devil. The doctor really does not have any control.

More than 83,000 drug representatives in this country alone go to doctors' offices to convince them that they need particular drugs for their patients. If doctors were trained, they would know what drugs are needed for our health. Billions of dollars are spent to influence people, who have no medical knowledge on what drugs they need for their bodies. Sometimes the medical doctors do not have a choice on what to recommend because patients demand certain things they have seen on television.

The following quotes were made by doctors in prominent positions concerning drugs and the drug industry:

1) *"The cause of most disease is the poisonous drugs physicians superstitiously give in order to effect a cure"* Charles E. Page, M.D.

2) R.T. Trall, M.D. stated that, *"Drugs medications consist in employing, as remedies for disease, those things which produce disease in well persons. Its materia medica is simply a lot of drugs or chemicals or dye-stuffs in a word poisons. All are incompatible with vital matter; all produce disease when brought in contact in any manner with the living; all are poisons."* Dr. Trall taught this in a two and a half hour lecture to members of congress and the medical profession, delivered at the Smithsonian Institute in Washington, D.C.

3) *"Every drug increases and complicates the patient's condition"* Robert Henderson, M.D.

4) *"Every educated physician knows that most diseases are not appreciably helped by medicine"* Richard C. Cabot, M.D.

5) *"The person who takes medicine must recover twice, once from the disease and once from the medicine"* William Osler, M.D.

6.) Dr. Elmer Lee, past Vice President for the Academy of Medicine, stated, *"Medical practice has neither philosophy nor common sense to recommend it. In sickness the body is already loaded with impurities. By taking drug medicines*

---

more impurities are added, thereby the case is further embarrassed and harder to cure."

7) "*Our figures show approximately four and one half million hospital admissions annually due to the adverse reactions to drugs. Further, the average hospital patient has as much as thirty percent chance, depending how long he is in, of doubling his stay due to adverse drug reactions*" Milton Silverman, M.D., Professor of Pharmacology at the University of California.

8) "*Why would a patient swallow a poison because he is ill, or take that which would make a well man sick*" L.F. Kebler, M.D.

9) "*We are prone to thinking of drug abuse in terms of the male population and illicit drugs such as heroin, cocaine, and marijuana. It may surprise you to learn that a greater problem exists with millions of women dependent on legal prescription drugs*" Robert Mendelsohn, M.D.

10) "*The greatest part of all chronic disease is created by the suppression of acute disease by drug poisoning*" Dr. Henry Lindlahr.

The system needs to change its operation to benefit the Saints of God and not destroy the body. Paul said in Galatians 5:19-21 that by being on a pharmaceutical drug of any type then you cannot enter the Kingdom of heaven. The term "witchcraft" in verse 20 means sorcery or pharmakeia (meaning pharmacy in English). The church should be in the position to prevent diseases, but it is currently promoting a diseased state based on the influence of the world's system.

Revelation 18:23c reads, "*For your merchants were the great men of the Earth; for with thy sorcery were all the nations deceived.*" "Sorcery" means pharmaceuticals. Verse 24 states that, "*In her was found the blood of prophets and of saints and all that was slain upon the Earth.*"

The drug Vioxx killed thousands of people and the church never mentioned it because the church is afraid to talk about system (the world) that is influenced by Satan. Revelation 18 is the chapter in which heaven rejoices because of the fall of the Babylonian Empire. The medical doctors' quotes above are saying that the drug industry is going to slowly destroy mankind.

The municipality, our water system, is filled with medications that we expel through waste. For example, the body only uses 20 percent of the drug that you take and the other 80 percent goes into our water system. We do not have a purification system that can actually destroy the drugs/medications that we expel. You do not have to be on a drug to be affected. Whatever you put on the skin will be absorbed into the flesh. Government inspectors have found that our water systems have quite a bit of drugs in them. For example, Washington, D.C. and New York have more than 15 different types of drugs in their water. The devil has created a powerful weapon against our environmental system that is harmful to the body (God's sanctuary).

Doctors and Suicide

The *Oxford Journal on Occupational Medicine* reports that medical doctors commit suicide more than any other profession in this country. "Last year, more than 400 doctors in this country committed suicide. Thousands of doctors try to kill themselves every year but do not succeed and even more think about suicide because of their work environment," reports Dr. Schemhammer, an instructor at Harvard Medical School and Brigham Women's Hospital in Boston.

Many of us have family who work in the medical field. We need to pray for our men and women who are in the system. An article in *USA Today*, written December 13, 2006, reported that, "…nursing homes and hospitals are not doing enough to prevent serial killers on their staff." Fifty doctors and four nurses were convicted for killing over 2,100 people. Investigators are saying that up to 5,400 serial killers may be in our hospitals; but they do not have sufficient evidence to convict. Serial killers kill just for pleasure. They have the intent to harm.

The Health Care System

The church needs to pray for our men and women who work in the world's health care system. When we go into the hospitals, we always pray for our sick and loved ones. We also need to pray for the professional staff.

This part of the book is not meant to insinuate that we should not utilize the health care system. There is some good in the system. We also need to be vigilant and aware that there is also harm in the system. We need to question our doctors and nurses. When visiting a doctor, our elderly should be escorted by a responsible party from the church if a family member is not available. Even the elderly are on unnecessary medications. Research shows that more than 75 percent of the elderly are taking the wrong medication. The church needs to have an overseer of the sanctuary of God. There are ways that we can turn diseases around without being on drugs/medications. We have to check the prescriptions and research the medications that doctors are recommending.

Many people who pay the most money and offer the most tithes are often those who work in the medical system. We have to be brave and speak against evil and wrongdoings. We have to live with faith, and know and understand that God will protect us if we are telling the truth. If you are afraid to teach the truth, then maybe you need to step aside and allow someone with confidence and a brave heart who God has called in the Ministry, to do the talking.

The US is ranked number 19 on the list which ranks the treatment of diseases in developing countries' medical systems, and number 35 worldwide. Cuba and Canada are higher on the list. However, the US' emergency medicine is ranked 1st on the list. The US has excellent response to trauma but ranks low for diseases. Diseases are developed in the body over a period of time, while trauma occurs without warning. For example, doctors in the US can easily stitch the body from a car accident or give you medications for pain.

There is evidence, not only from this book, but also research from others, which indicates that diseases can be cured by changing your lifestyle. Let us pray for our children, neighbors, and even our enemies who are in the medical system because we put God's sanctuary in their hands. Every day that the church doors open, someone needs to be praying for the medical system. Read our *Statement of Faith* to fully understand how to deal with diseases.

As long as you are alive, you have an opportunity to turn your life around and live healthier. Everything that is in this book has already been announced in the news media around the world. However, many of us missed it because we did not believe that diseases were curable. Make sure that your doctor is not depressed or is not a drug addict. Researchers have found that many doctors suffer from alcoholism, depression, and drug addiction. Make sure that the doctors are operating on the correct side of your body. Doctors are in a system which is not conducive to mental and moral health. Often times, they do not get enough rest before they do surgeries around-the-clock. Pray for the doctors. Ask questions and get a record of their medical performance.

A doctor is not God. Do not lift them up like Simon the sorcerer in Acts 8:9-11, who used medicine/drugs/magical art. Many believed that he was some type of god. Churches believe that God trains medical professionals to put you on a drug that is going to have side effects. God would never put anything in your body that is going to cause diseases. He is a God of Health and not a God of diseases. Please pray and lift up the doctors and nurses who are on the front line so that they can create a healthy environment to carry out their duties.

*   *   *   *   *   *

FOODS AND RECIPES

Vegetarian Recipes

"And God said, 'See I have given you every herb that yields seed which is on the face of all the earth, and every tree whose fruit yields seed, to you it shall be for food'" (Genesis 1:29).

Hummus
1-3/4 cups garbanzo beans (chickpeas)
6 cups water
3 garlic cloves, peeled
1-1/4 cups tahini paste
1 teaspoon dried cumin
1 teaspoon chili powder (or to taste)
1/3 cup lemon juice
2 tablespoons olive oil

Wash garbanzo beans (chickpeas) and soak in cold water for 24-

hours. Place garbanzo beans, with their soaking liquid, in a large saucepan and bring to a boil. Simmer for 2 hours, skimming off any debris that may surface. Drain garbanzo beans, reserving 1/4 cup liquid, and refresh in cold water. Process until smooth. Add garlic, tahini, spices and Braggs Amino Acid, lemon juice and olive oil. Reprocess and adjust seasoning.

Variations
If you like a spicier hummus, add a small red chili (chopped) or a pinch of cayenne pepper, or try a little cumin for a more exotic variation.

Radish Wheels
12 nice sized radishes, cleaned
2 shallots, minced
1 clove of garlic, finely minced soy mayonnaise
Dash of pepper
Chop the radishes. Add all the other ingredients. Mix well. Add enough mayo to coat the mixture. Cut the crusts of several slices of bread. Roll out the bread until it is flat with a rolling pin. Spread Dijon mustard lightly on the bread. Spread a couple of spoonfuls of the radishes mixture over the bread. Roll up and secure with a toothpick. When all the radish mixture has been used, lay the rolls on a tray, cover tightly with plastic wrap, and refrigerate for an hour or more. Remove and slice into wheels. Yummy!

Veggie Chop
1 cup chopped cauliflower
1 cup chopped broccoli
1 cup chopped carrots

1 cup chopped little green onions with their tails
1 cucumber peeled and seeded
2 tablespoons liquid raw honey
1/2 cup plain soy yogurt
1 generous teaspoon curry powder
6 pita bread - (no wheat, no dairy, no preservatives—whole grain only)

Mix chopped veggies together in a bowl. In a blender, place the cucumber, honey, curry powder and yogurt. Puree until smooth. Pour over veggies in the bowl. Refrigerate overnight or for three or four hours to give the flavors a chance to meld. Cut the Pitas in half. Warm them for just a few seconds first, then cut and open them. It seems to work better. Stuff each pita half with a generous portion of the veggie chop. Serves four to six people.

Lettuce Rolls
4 scallions thinly sliced
1 cup bean sprouts lightly chopped
6 water chestnuts chopped
4 radishes chopped
1 stalk celery thinly sliced
1 small carrot cut in half lengthwise and thinly sliced
2 tablespoons Ranch Dressing (vegetarian, no preservatives, no dairy) or alternative dressing (such as olive oil and Bragg's Amino Acid)
dash of cayenne pepper
6 washed and dried lettuce leaves

Mix all ingredients together except for the lettuce leaves. Divide mixture evenly between the lettuce leaves. Roll up and secure with a toothpick. Chill.

Cream of Carrot Soup
3 cups carrot juice - bought or fresh
1 whole, ripe avocado
Alfalfa sprouts
Blend juice and avocado in a blender. Divide into bowls. Garnish with alfalfa sprouts. Serve chilled.

Raw, Stuffed Pepper Cups
1 cup chopped zucchini
1 cup shredded carrot
1 cup bean sprouts
1/2 cup chopped celery
1/2 cup chopped radishes
soy mayo to moisten
6 sweet red peppers, deveined and seeds removed
Cut the tops off the peppers. Gently remove the veins and shake out seeds. Mix all veggies together in a bowl. Add enough mayo to moisten. Stuff into peppers. Replace tops on peppers. Chill and serve.

Carrot, Ginger Salad or Pita Stuffing
2 cups of grated carrot
1/2 teaspoon of freshly grated ginger
1/3 cup of seedless raisins
Soy mayo to moisten
Combine all ingredients in a bowl. Add enough mayo to moisten or more if you like. Chill. Line individual bowls or half pita pockets with lettuce leaves. Fill with the carrot mixture. Serve chilled.

Sweet Autumn Salad
4 apples
4 pears
5 ripe bananas
1/2 cup raisins
1/2 cup date pieces
1/3 cup apple juice
Slice and mix together.
Moisten the mixture with apple juice. Serve.

Dr. Dail's Cabbage Delight
1/2 medium cabbage (shredded)
5 sprigs of parsley
1 ounce Sesame oil
1/4 teaspoon cayenne pepper
1 ounce Bragg's Amino Acid
1 ounce UME plum vinegar
1 teaspoon garlic powder
1/2 teaspoon onion powder
Mix all ingredients together. Chill and serve, OR let sit for two or
more hours to marinate.

Live Food Breakfast
8 ounces of raw oatmeal (not instant)
2 ounces of shaved coconut

2 ounces of raisins or
2 ounces of unsulferated chopped dates
6 ounces of apple juice, soy milk, almond milk, or rice milk
2 tablespoons Flaxseed meal (freshly ground)
Optional: 1/2 banana
Mix ingredients, let sit for 2 minutes, and enjoy!

Dail's Dandelion Salad

1/2 pound tender, fresh dandelion greens (produce department)
1/2 cup thinly sliced red onions, 2 tomatoes, cut in fourths
1/4 pound soy cheese, 1/4 teaspoon cayenne pepper
1/4 cup salad oil, tablespoon vinegar
1 teaspoon dill
Wash the dandelion greens carefully. Drain well and cut into pieces.
Add the onions, tomatoes, and cheese. Toss to mix. Make a salad
dressing by mixing the pepper, salad oil, vinegar, and dill. Dress the
salad, toss, and serve.

*NOTE: If you pick the dandelions, make sure that you take the dandelion
greens from a lawn that has not been treated with pesticides or anti-growth
hormones. Many lawn fertilizers also contain weed-control hormones.*

PETEGAT FOOD
(Person Eating To Edify God's Amazing Temple)

<u>Ingredients:</u>
8 ounces of liquid (organic Soy, Almond, or Rice milk)
4 ounces Spring Water
1 pack Stevia or (1 pack) Sweetleaf Stevia Plus
1 tablespoon Goji berries (not Goji juice)
1 tablespoon Flax Seed
Use up to 20 grams of plant-based protein powder

1/2 scoop Greens First

1 level tablespoon Flaxseed (whole)

Mix flaxseed and Goji berries in coffee grinder for 25 seconds. Add the Soy, Rice, or Almond milk (no dairy) and the water in a mixer or shaker container. Do not grind the flaxseeds, add it to the food whole (by chewing the whole flaxseed you will be adding more saliva for better digestion). Add the rest of the ingredients, shake vigorously, and enjoy.

The world's greatest and perfect food combination— by Dr. James A. Dail, Sr.

REFORMATION HEALING MINISTRIES
TESTIMONIES

Dear Dr. Dail:

Thank you so much for saving my life. I was in bad health when I first started your program. My liver, kidney, red blood cells, white blood cells, eyes, lungs, knees, feet, and ears were operating on low. The only good thing was my cholesterol. I do not know why it was good. My blood sugar was 252.

Today I am much better. My blood sugar is 112-100-98; and all of my other problems have cleared up.

—Loraine Williams
Forestville, MD

Dear Dr. Dail,

My name is Stormi Burns and I am a junior at South View High School. Unfortunately, due to my father's sickness, my first years of high school were terrible. I was unable to enjoy my freshman and sophomore years the way I wanted to; but "now" thanks to you, I can and I will have the best junior and senior year ever. I am sooooo thankful to have pastors like mine that would allow a wonderful person like you to help us in a time of need. Thanks 2 U, I have had the best Thanksgiving ever.

Thank you so much. I pray your family is blessed from generation to generation.

—Stormi

P.S. You are the answer to my prayers.

"And now, Israel, what doth the Lord thy God require of thee, but to fear the Lord thy God, to walk in all thy ways, and to love Him, and to serve the Lord thy God with all thy heart and with all thy soul"(Deuteronomy 10:12).

*   *   *   *   *   *

Hi, my name is Ruth White. My sister and her husband came to South Carolina to bring me to Maryland to see Dr. James Dail. I heard a lot about this dynamic Neuropathy doctor from my sister, who lives in Maryland. Before I came to Maryland, I was in so much pain my husband would not let me go to the mailbox, which is directly in front of my house. I experienced constant pain day and night. I became depressed.

After meeting with Dr. Dail, he shared a new type of eating habit with me—starting with the foods I should eat. I started immediately. Within the first week I saw results. Not only did I notice a change, but so did my family. Five of my toes were turned downward for years. Then one Sunday, I looked down and they were back to normal. I was on 13 different types of medication: 3 for high blood pressure, 3 for diabetes, etc. I stayed in Maryland for three months. When I returned to South Carolina, my doctor took me off some of the medications and instructed me to continue doing what I was doing.

I believe, had I not met Dr. Dail, I would not be here today. I can truly say that I do NOT have any pain: and I give GOD the praise for this man of GOD that loves people and is concerned about their health.

—Ruth White
St. Matthews, South Carolina

"Trust in the Lord with all thine heart; and lean not unto thine own understanding" (Proverb 3:5).

"When you sit down to eat with a ruler consider carefully what is before you; and put a knife to your throat if you are a man given to appetite. Do not desire his delicacies, for they are deceptive foods" (Proverbs 23:1-3).

* * * * * *

After following Dr. James Dail's advise, I went to my doctor for a check up in July of 2008. Everything checked out normal including my A1C test on my glucose level and blood pressure reading. My doctor said a couple of times that I was a success story. Not many people will follow the instructions given to them from heath practitioners; and because I followed the instructions, I am now called a success story. I am free from diabetes and no longer need medication.

—Bishop Edwin J. Derensbourg, III

Visit www.jamesdailministries.org for more testimonies

OVERSEER AND FOUNDER OF REFORMATION HEALING MINISTRIES INTERNATIONAL, LLC

JAMES A. DAIL, SR., PhD, ThD, ND

James A. Dail, Sr., PhD, ThD, ND is an anointed man of God. He is an accomplished Doctor of Theology, ministering the Word of God; and a Doctor of Naturopathy, teaching Health and Healing God's Way. He is also an author of several books and articles on optimal health and healing through a natural, holistic, spiritual approach.

Born in Greenville, North Carolina on January 4, 1947, Dr. James Dail, Sr. is one of 15 children—six boys and nine girls. He was raised by loving parents, Clarence and Esther Dail, and educated in Lenoir County, North Carolina, where he graduated from high school in 1965.

Dr. Dail entered the US Air Force immediately upon graduating from high school. His military service took him on assignments throughout the world where he served in various positions from Electrical Superintendent to Facilities Management. He served in Vietnam and was awarded several accommodation and combat medals. He retired from the Air Force in May 1987 after 22 years of dedicated and outstanding service.

His formal education includes an Associates degree from Community College of the Air Force. He completed his undergraduate studies at Golden Gate University of San Francisco, City College of Chicago, Averett University of Virginia, University of Maine at Presque Isle, and Tanana Valley Community College of Alaska during his Air Force career.

Prior to dedicating full-time work in the area of Health and Nutrition, Dr. Dail was a successful entrepreneur. A natural businessman, Dr. Dail built The Dail Management Corporation, a company he owned with over 105 employees. His corporation received several contracts with such companies as Pepsi Cola, Montgomery Wards, Crown, Cork and Seal, US Postal Service, Bally's Gym, and Unisys.

Utmost in Dr. Dail's life was a concern for health and nutrition. With his God-given abilities, he began to teach health and nutrition while managing his businesses. Finally, Dr. Dail realized that God had called him to teach the "Theology of Health." He started Reformation Health Ministries and Trinity Wellness Center based in Silver Spring, M.D.

Dr. Dail has been practicing nutrition for more than 22 years. He received his Doctor of Naturopathy (ND) certification from Trinity College in Warsaw, Indiana. He also became a licensed minister of the Gospel in 1998. To further enhance his ministry, he received a Master's and a Doctorate Degree in Theology from Breakthrough Bible College, where he currently serves as Professor and Dean of the Christian Health and Healing Academy.

After becoming a minister of the Gospel in 1998, along with his many years of teaching Health, the Holy Spirit prompted Dr. Dail to teach "Health and Healing God's Way." He has conducted seminars and workshops for over 15 years throughout the US, Guyana, Europe, and Africa. His seminar and workshop presentations cover such topics as "Spirituality and Nutrition," "Health & Wellness God's Way," "Natural Health Food Demonstrations," "Eating for A's" (raising children's grades), "Nutrition for Optimal Health," and "Fasting." Dr. Dail consistently places emphasis on the physical body and states, "As church leaders, we need to include discussions and teachings on the physical body along with the mind and the spirit—as the physical body is the first echelon member of the body of Christ." He has written many magazine articles on health and healing.

His credentials in the Natural Health field are numerous. They range from being a Certified Nutritional Consultant (CNC), a

Certified Natural Health Professional (CNHP), and a Registered Naturopath from the Council on Naturopathic Registration and Accreditation, Inc., as well as a Colon Hydro Therapist. He is Board Certified by the American Naturopathic Medical Association, and is also a member of the American College of Iridology.

Education and remaining abreast in his field are very important to Dr. Dail. He puts in numerous research hours on health and wellness. This knowledge is reflected in his many Board affiliations, which include the Medical Advisory Board with Novavit, Inc., Barlow Herbal Inc., and ForMor International Inc. He is also a member of the International Anti-aging Conference.

He has three adult children—Tonya, a Pediatrician; Sherrie, a Speech Pathologist; and James, Jr., a Nuclear Engineer and Entrepreneur.

Dr. Dail is an Elder of the United Christian Fellowship of Palmdale, California, under the leadership of Dr. Edwin Derensbourg, III. He is ordained by God to educate His people about prevention, maintenance, and healing of His temple—God's Way.

Future Books & Products

FUTURE VOLUMES OF
"TOOLS FOR HEALTH AND HEALING GOD'S WAY"
BY DR. JAMES A. DAIL, SR.

Volumes 2 - 10

2. Tithing and Giving are a Major Foundation for Health and Healing (Volume 2)

3. The Church's Responsibility to the Body, God's Sanctuary (Volume 3)

4. Children, Women, and Men's Health According to God's Plan (Volume 4)

5. The Weapons Used by the Adversary to Destroy the Body of Christ (Volume 5)

6. God's Spiritual Principal for Health and Healing of His Sanctuary—Our Body (Volume 6)

7. Sexual Health in Marriages (Volume 7)

8. Diseases and Their Remedies (Volume 8)

9. Stress, Worry, and Negative Emotions (Volume 9)

10. Bible Commentaries on Health and Healing God's Way (Volume 10)

FUTURE BOOKS
BY DR. JAMES A. DAIL, SR.

"Food Prepared to Glorify the Temple of God"
"Health Tidbits that are Beneficial to the Children of God"

PRODUCTS FOR SALE

DVDs
"Foods Prepared to Glorify the Temple of God"
Dr. James A. Dail, Sr.

"Vulnerable Place of Attack"
Dr. James A. Dail, Sr.

CDs
"Health and Wellness God's Way"

Books, DVDs, and CDs can be purchased online at
www.jamesdailministries.org

Supporters

SUPPORTERS

The tools in this book have been taught in churches nationally and internationally, including the following:

Annalope Valley Christian Center
Dr. Thomas and Donna Pickens
Lancaster, CA

Arise Ministries
Pastor Robert Blackwell
Baton Rouge, LA

Breakthrough Bible College
Dr. Anthony Mays, President
Temple Hills, MD

Christian Bible Church
Pastor Rudy White
Missouri City, TX

Church of the Living God
Biship Connie Banza
Chicago, IL

Creflo Dollar Ministries
Dr. Creflo A. Dollar & Taffi L. Dollar
College Park, GA

Covenant Christian Center
Pastor Charles and Barbara Lewis
New Haven, CT

Cumberland Christian Center
Dr. E. B. and Rosa Herman
Fayetteville, NC

Established Covenant Church
Pastors Kenny and Cynthia Barbour
Richmond, VA

Excellence Christian Church
Pastors Russell & Yuvetta Cash
Bowie, MD

Family Life Christian Church International
Pastors Ray and Sharon McQueen
Lynchburg, VA

First Church of Wyandanch Ministries
Bishop and Mrs. Michael Talbert
Wyandanch, NY

Go Tell It Ministries Worldwide
Bishop Corletta A. Vaughn
Detroit, MI

Greater Guiding Star, UHC
Pastor Joseph M. Williams, Sr.
Goldsboro, NC

Holy Hope Heritage Baptist Church
Dr. William Revely
Detroit, MI

Jericho City of Praise
Apostle Betty Peebles
Landover, MD

Judah Temple A.M.E. Zion
Pastor Scot C. & First Lady Sharon Moore
Mitchellville, MD

Judea Baptist Church
Pastor Linwood Dean
Hempstead, NY

Life Christian Center
Pastor Anne Jones
Las Vegas, NV

Mount of Blessing Christian Center
Pastors Demetri and Nicole Bradley
Richmond, VA

Mount Sinai Church
Pastors Richie and Terry Sessoms
Portsmouth, VA

Oasis of Victory Christian Church International
Pastor James O. Spence, Jr.
Lexington Park, MD

Peaceful Zion Missionary Baptist Church
Dr. CP Preston, Jr.
Miami, FL

Pentecostal Churches of Christ
*Holy Convocation and Joint College of Bishops
Leadership Training*
Bishop J. Delano Ellis, II and Pastor Sabrina J. Ellis
Cleveland, OH

Progressive Church Ministries
Pastors Don and Karyn Massey
Clinton, MD

Providence Harvest United Church of God in Christ
Bishop Manuel Stancil
Raleigh, NC

Redeeming Word Christian Center International
Pastors Ed and Yvette Brinson
Ft. Lauderdale, FL

Revival Temple Church
Bishop Milton L. Carter
Washington, D.C.

River of Life Christian Center
Pastor Larry Locus
Kinston, NC

Spirit of Faith Christian Center
Drs. Michael & Dee Dee Freeman
Brandywine, MD

The Teleconference Ministry
Pastor Jimmie McDonald
Grapevine, TX

United Christian Fellowship
Bishop Edwin J. and Venita M. Derensbourg, III
Palmdale, CA

United Faith Fellowship Church
Pastor Berta Newsome
Meadville, PA

Victory Christian Ministries International
Pastors Tony and Cynthia Brazelton
Suitland, MD

Word of Restoration Christian Fellowship
Pastor Charles E. Perry, Jr.
Rosharon, TX

Visit www.jamesdailministries.org for a list of additional supporters.

CONTACT US

Dr. James A. Dail, Sr. and Reformation Healing Ministries International are looking forward to working with you to help you reach your goal of obtaining optimal health.

REFORMATION HEALING MINISTRIES INTERNATIONAL
2101 Timber Ridge Road
Monroe, NC 28112
(301) 868-0262
Website: www.jamesdailministries.org
Email: drdail@jamesdailministries.org